*THE HERITAGE OF KITTY HAWK*

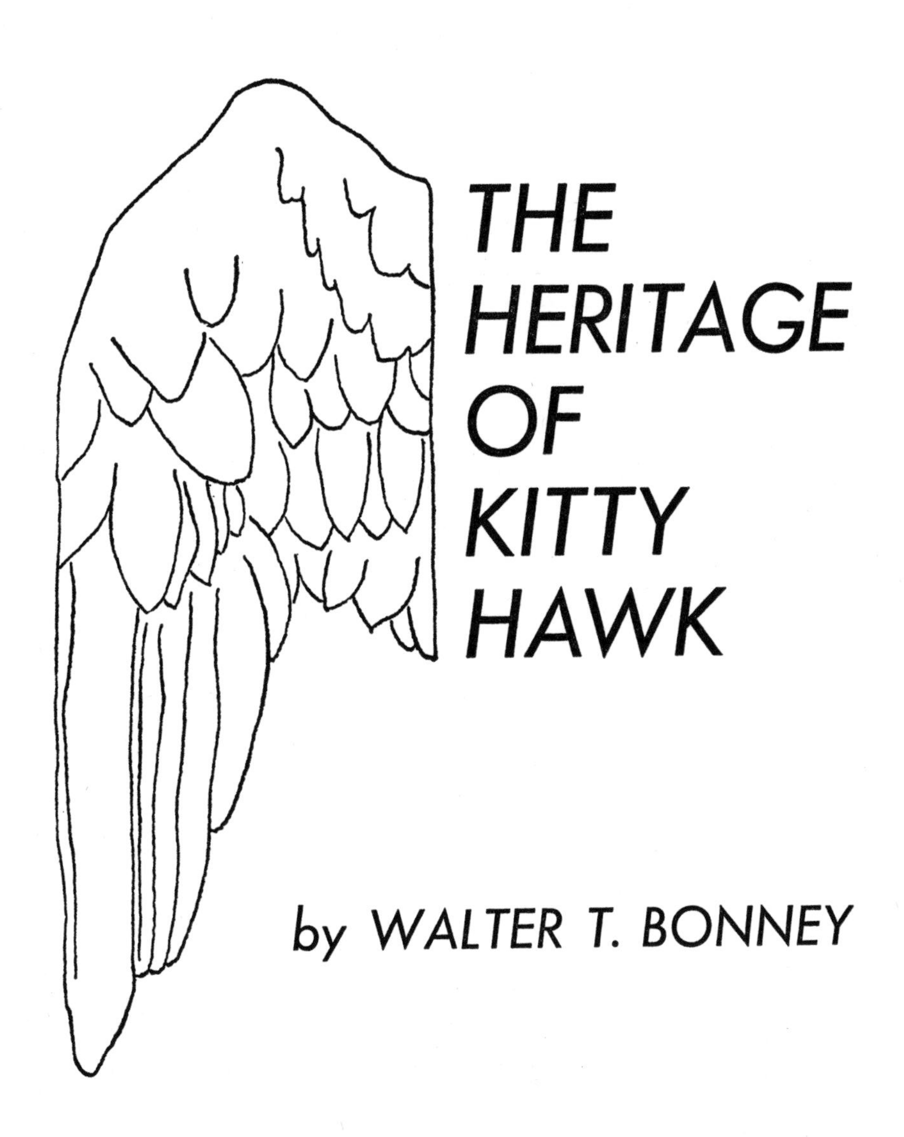

# THE HERITAGE OF KITTY HAWK

by WALTER T. BONNEY

NEW YORK

W · W · NORTON & COMPANY · INC ·

First Edition

Library of Congress Catalog Card No. 62-10093


Published simultaneously in the Dominion of Canada
by George J. McLeod Limited, Toronto

*Book designed by James J. Harvin*

PRINTED IN THE UNITED STATES OF AMERICA
FOR THE PUBLISHERS BY THE VAIL-BALLOU PRESS, INC.

1 2 3 4 5 6 7 8 9

To: Richard Schley Boutelle, Jr.
John Frederick Boutelle, II

Born August 3, 1960, the sons of the late Richard Schley Boutelle, whose eventful life spanned the era from Orville and Wilbur Wright to Yuri Gagarin; whose career was devoted to furthering winged flight, and whose sustained support made this book possible.

# CONTENTS

# PREFACE

"Heritage of Kitty Hawk" first appeared serially in "The Pegasus," published by the Fairchild Engine and Airplane Corporation—since renamed the Fairchild Stratos Corporation. The first five chapters titled, "Prelude to Kitty Hawk," were published in 1953 (when man was still struggling to reach Mach 2 flight speed); the remainder, given the name of this book, followed in the period, April, 1955—October, 1957 (the last chapter in the same month Sputnik I went into orbit).

I wish here to acknowledge my profound gratitude to the Fairchild Stratos Corporation and more specifically to its president, Edward G. Uhl, for the permission granted to publish in book form these writings and illustrations.

In addition, I wish to acknowledge the very great help and encouragement given by many people. The dozen mentioned here comprise by no means all who contributed importantly to this undertaking. Within the Fairchild organization there were: William G. Key, editor of "The Pegasus" in 1953 and for years thereafter; Ralph G. Platt, who followed as editor; James J. Fisher, art director of "The Pegasus"; C. Leo DeOrsey, and the late Richard S. Boutelle, long-time Company president. Then there were Hugh L. Dryden, at the time Director of the National Advisory Committee for Aeronautics, who read so perceptively the first drafts; Grace Bogart, then librarian of the NACA, who aided mightily in searching for source material; Paul E. Garber of the National Air Museum, who contributed much of fact and illustration, and Major James M. Sunderman of the Air Force, who gave so much encouragement to the compilation into book form of the several chapters. Finally, and most of all, enduring thanks to my wife, Dorothy, and daughter, Jean, for their patience and affectionate understanding when the words were coming hard.

*Pacific Palisades, California*
*April, 1962*

# FOREWORD

Dreams, visions, creeping progress towards the goal . . . and then accomplishment! Untold millenniums when man paused from his plodding along the track to look enviously at the birds, soaring and wheeling in seemingly effortless flight. It is the same today. Pelicans by the score fly up and down the Florida beaches in single file, "as if framed together."

Centuries when man had visions of "magickal vapours" and other occult devices that would solve the secret of flight. Because of the primitive sources of power then available, it is not strange that the devices concocted for man-carrying flight were strange and wonderful. As strange and wonderful, almost, as the anti-gravitational, faster-than-light chariots which our present-day visionaries and television producers propose to carry to the outermost galaxy of the firmament.

The United States of America was a lusty adolescent nation before the time had come when the dreams and visions of flight began to assume the shape and substance of an attainable possibility. To be sure, there had been men before who pointed the way, like Leonardo, men who were centuries ahead of their fellow man. It required hardly a century of creeping progress, though, during which developments crowded fast one upon another, until—on December

17, 1903—there came that crowning achievement above the shifting sands of Kitty Hawk, North Carolina, the achievement of controlled, powered, heavier-than-air flight by two self-taught bicycle makers, the sons of an Ohio preacher.

# THE HERITAGE OF KITTY HAWK

# 1/ THE DREAMERS

*"The way of the air remains,*
*By the sky we will essay to go."*
*Ovid*

In the dream world of legend and mythology the ways of flight were many. There were the winged men of Egypt, and the winged bulls of Assyria. Sinbad the Sailor had his great Roc, and the Arabs had their magic flying carpet. The pre-Christian Capnobates of the Middle East traveled "by smoke," and we remember the tragedy of Icarus, whose wings came unstuck when he flew too close to the sun.

Nor may we forget Pegasus, perhaps the most fabulous of the winged steeds of yore.

Among earliest references to flight by man is that found in the Sanscrit epic *Mahabharata* which recounts, in curiously modern terms, that: "Krishna's enemies sought the aid of the demons who built an aerial chariot with sides of iron and clad with wings. The chariot was driven through the sky till it stood over Dwarakha, where Krishna's followers dwelt, and from there it hurled down upon the city missiles that destroyed everything on which they fell."

Here in the Americas, the Incas knew of Ayar Utso who grew wings and flew to the sun. The Teutons had Wieland the Smith who made himself a dress with wings. Clad in it, he rose and descended against the wind, and in spite of it. The Finns remember Ilmarinen who "forged an eagle of fire" which he flew on his exploits. Nevertheless for centuries to come it would be as was written in *Proverbs:*

> *"There are three things which are too wonderful for me,*
> *Yea, four which I know not:—"*

and listed as the first

> *"The way of an eagle in the air;"*

From the fourth century before Christ until the 15th century, there was produced a mass, or mess, of apocrypha. In this category will be found stories about the wooden dove constructed by that learned geometer, Archytas. Possessed of such special qualities as an "aura of spirit," even this marvel of the pre-Christian era, "if it fell, it could not raise itself up any more."

In the time of Nero, it has been recorded by Antonius Byerlink, Simon the Magician rose up to assert his superiority over Saint Paul. As the story goes, he prevailed upon the aid of certain demons and actually lifted himself into the air. Saint Paul prayed him down again; and, at the climax of the headlong descent, Simon the Magician broke his neck.

Then there was the Saracen who, in the 11th Century and in the presence of his emperor, Comnenus, attempted to fly around the hippodrome of Constantinople. Cousin writes that he took off from a tower in the midst of the hippodrome, clad in a long white robe stiffened with rods so as to spread and catch the breeze. At first he "rose like a bird," but then, "the weight of his body having more power to drag him down than his artificial wings had to sustain him, he broke his bones, and his evil plight was such that he did not long survive."

Oliver, the monk of Malmesbury, was one who, in 1065, made himself a pair of Daedalian wings, and thus managed effectively to shorten his life. Johann Müller made an iron bug in the early 15th Century and sent it out to welcome Emperor Charles V on one of his victorious returns to Nürnberg. The only thing that is really wrong with this last tale is that Müller died just about 25 years before Emperor Charles V was born!

In 13th Century England one finds Roger Bacon, a Franciscan

Friar, who was not only a philosopher of parts but something of a scientist. In his consideration of the problems and possibilities of flight, his thinking ran counter to the orthodox views of his time, which in essence, might have been summarized as follows: "It is not necessarily impossible for human beings to fly, but it so happens that God has not vouchsafed them the knowledge of how to do it: hence it follows that any one who claims that he can fly must have sought the aid of the Devil. To attempt to fly is therefore sinful." Bacon's offerings, despite his prophetic visions of aeronautical progress in the future, showed no great advance beyond the times of Archytas. He, too, depended upon "aetherial air" and "liquid fire" in describing the aerial vehicles he proposed, but failed, to construct.

Towering high above the mists and vapors of 15th Century legend and doubtful history is that giant, that incredible genius, Leonardo da Vinci. From his notebooks, it is clear that for years he thought solution to the problem of human flight would come from successful imitation of the behavior of flying creatures. Moreover, it is equally true that for 400 years thereafter this identical belief would still be espoused by many. In fact, even now when winged transport has become commonplace, and 4,000 mph speeds have been officially chronicled, man continues to look to the sky and envy the birds for their perfect mastery of the art of flight. To digress a moment, read what James L. G. Fitzpatrick wrote on this thought, in the early fifties, in the "Technology Review" of MIT:—

"The flight of birds and insects has endlessly challenged man and defied his genius for imitation. Their mode of flight, by gliding and the beating of wings, still provides interesting possibilities for the improvement of modern aircraft, and for the extension of air-transport services to fields as yet untouched . . . Their landing and take-off maneuverabilities are the envy of every designer. The flight of small birds over thousands of miles of open ocean is a marvel of air-worthiness and economy of power. In such flights, birds frequently perform miracles of navigation as, for example, pinpointing a small ocean island. Their mastery of the air, the surface of the sea, and, in some cases, the waters beneath it, are the inspiration of countless inventors.

"That the bird was man's teacher in the difficult art of flight is well attested by history. There is some doubt, however, about the conditions under which we students left nature's flying school. Did we graduate or are we still truants from the early grades?"

More to the point, Leonardo's invention of the aerial screw, or propeller, with which he equipped his small, sometimes successful helicopter models, was a contribution to the ages. From it has come modern marine transport as well as airplane and helicopter flight. Hardly less important was his invention of the parachute. On the theoretical side, he anticipated—by two centuries—the findings of Newton, when he wrote that "the movement of the air against a fixed thing is as great as the movement of the movable thing against the air which is immovable."

After the perceptive anticipations of Leonardo there was little aeronautical progress, or even speculation, for some 200 years. Of those proposals which finally did come, none merits recollection today except as evidence of the manner in which the learned men intended to harness their knowledge.

Consider the 17th Century Jesuit, Gaspar Schott, who was known for his work in physics. Observing that inasmuch as empty eggshells were extremely light, and also that dew rose from the grass under the morning sun, he speculated that the correct way to raise a respectable payload into the air was to assemble a sufficient number of dew-filled eggshells, and, from their lifting capacity, soar into the heavens.

In 1662, in England, King Charles II granted a charter for the formation of the Royal Society to give status to the hitherto private meetings of "divers worthy persons inquisitive into natural philosophy." Among the early members of that body was the Lord Bishop of Chester, John Wilkins, who listed four ways by which man could hope to fly: With the spirits of angels, with the help of fowls, with wings fastened to the body, and with a flying chariot. If this smacks of necromancy, one must remember that Wilkins' was the voice of 17th Century science proclaiming that the seemingly impossible was in reality not impossible, and that only lack of knowledge was holding men back.

The work of the middle 17th Century Italian scientist, Giovanni Borelli, is remembered by few and, more's the pity, attracted little attention from his contemporaries. It was he who observed that: "It is impossible that men should be able to fly craft by their own strength." His studies of bird flight were painstaking, and were directed at the demolition of mathematically impossible ideas. The work of this outstandingly intelligent and far-sighted man found little favor, though, with all but a very few of those who continued the quest. Instead, they preferred to believe that the key to flight was to learn how to do it like a bird.

One theorist of the 19th Century wrote: "One point I have studied and that is, How can a twenty pound wild goose carry itself so easily? Weigh every feather you can pick from a wild goose and they will not weigh one pound. Now if the feathers can be picked off from the goose he can come no nearer flying than we can.

"So there we have it clearly demonstrated that one pound of goose feathers can pick up 19 pounds of goose and carry this 19 pounds and its one pound of feathers through space at about half a mile a minute.

"Now my theory is this, and it applies to all birds. Notice any bird when he suddenly starts to fly, and you will notice a lightning-like quiver of his feathers. I believe that this quiver causes the production of a negative force of magnetism, or some kind of force which pushes the bird from the earth—just the reverse of the loadstone. He then has only to use his wings to propel the body, for the magnetic earth-force does the lifting, and that is all produced by the feathers. If it were not, then the bird ought to fly when divested of his feathers. This is the force which should be looked for; because whoever discovers it will make a fortune."

In Portugal, in the early 18th Century, Friar Bartholomeu de Gusmão invented a "passarola" which won for him an annual pension of 600,000 reis, and a professorship in mathematics at the University of Coimbra. This generosity by the King was for an airship design—de Gusmão wisely declined ever to build it—which was lifted by a set of permanent magnets plus a quantity of electrified amber. Bellows were specified to provide a draft in the event the winds failed.

Emanuel Swedenborg, having invented a new religion, proceeded in the 18th Century to invent a flying machine which involved the use of wings . . . "hollow below in order to increase the force and velocity, take in the air, and make the resistance as great as may be required . . . they should be in the shape of birds' wings, or the sails of a windmill, or some such shape." Certainly, anyone wishing to build a Swedenborg airship had ample option as to design.

Somewhat earlier, the Frenchman, Besnier, had constructed what some regard as the first successful glider. Descriptions indicate it was an ornithopter contraption, with which he is supposed to have flapped his way safely from a garret window to the ground below, and straightaway turned his attention to other matters. In 1742, the Marquis de Bacqueville attached paddle-shaped wings to his arms and legs. So equipped he sought to fly across the river Seine, but instead plumped into a washerwoman's boat in the river, and broke both legs.

In 1783, Montgolfier climaxed his work with balloons when Pilâtre de Rozier made his first ascent. But, to quote Otto Lilienthal (*see Chapter III*): "The balloon has been of no assistance to real aviation; nay it may even be considered as a direct brake upon the progress of this technique, because it split up the energy and directed the investigation which should have been devoted to dynamical flight into wrong channels."

On the eve of the 19th Century, certainly man had still a long, long way to go before he would learn to fly. Lacking engines even remotely suitable, lacking metals light and strong, lacking even the most rudimentary knowledge of aerodynamics, he was still (except for the balloon) earthbound. Nevertheless, he continued to dream, and to find comfort in visions. He was beginning to learn some of the necessary knowledge that eventually would lead to flight. He was beginning to experiment.

In the century ahead, he would make great strides forward, until wise men would scan the skies and wait for the day when man-made flight would surely happen.

# 2 / THE EARLY EXPERIMENTERS

*He ne'er is crowned*
*With immortality—who fears to follow*
*Where airy voices lead.*

Keats

The year 1776 is memorable, but not only because it was the date our forefathers declared their independence of kings. In that year, too, Boulton and Watt produced their first effective steam engine; and, in the doing, sparked an industrial revolution which has yet to run its course. The steam engine indirectly deserves credit for hastening the advent of the airplane, because—although it never proved practicable as an aircraft engine—it caused men for the first time to think in terms of the existence of a mechanical power plant. Thus it diverted some of the wiser ones from further pursuit of that scientific will-o'-the-wisp which had men trying to fly by muscle power.

Among the first to propose an airplane propeller-driven by an engine, was Sir George Cayley. During his life, from 1773 to 1857, he made great contributions to aeronautics, not the least of which was his advocacy of an interchange of information by workers in the field, and, to further that end, the actual publication of his own writings on aeronautics.

Cayley's clear and simple statement of the problem of flight—"to make a surface support a given weight by the application of power to the resistance of air"—would, alone, justify his title as the father of British aeronautics. He was not the first to have studied the resistance offered by the air to a given surface; as early as 1661

Hooke had written a paper about "Resistance of Air to Bodyes Moved Through It." Nor was he the first to have calculated the surface area necessary to support a man flying in the air. That accomplishment must be credited to Karl F. Meerwin who published his work in 1784. When it came to his comments about the inability of man to fly by means of wings worked by muscle power, Cayley was only repeating the comments of 17th Century Borelli (*see Chapter I*).

What Cayley did which is especially memorable is that he fitted a collection of "whys" and "why-nots" into a sensible whole. Instead of contenting himself with telling men how not to attempt flight, he pointed the way toward ultimate success.

Even in the matter of power plants, Cayley was gifted with prescience. He foresaw the ultimate prime mover (a century ago they called it a "first mover") of the airplane to be the reciprocating engine. (Here again, the term of the day was different; Cayley called it an "explosion machine.") He was some 55 years ahead of his time, because it was not until 1865 that Lenoir completed his first practicable, though crude, gasoline engine.

Cayley's theorizing on the problems of aerodynamics included initial velocity, wing loads, bending movements, and the necessity for combining lightness and strength. He saw the need for streamline construction, and is credited with having an awareness that a cambered wing, rather than a flat surface, would be required. He conceived, as one solution to the problems at hand, the idea of biplane construction with struts and diagonal bracing. This biplane idea he used in building a glider, which he fitted with both horizontal and vertical rudders, the beginnings of today's airplane controls. "It was very beautiful to see this noble white bird sail majestically from the top of a hill to any given point of the plain below it, with perfect steadiness and safety," he wrote, in 1809.

Moreover, although there is no indication that Sir George ever entrusted his own bones to the glider, there is the contemporary account that a hired hand (one version has him a coachman; another, the gardener) was persuaded to make a flight . . . which ended in a crash resulting in no physical harm to the servant, but with great damage to the test pilot's enthusiasm for aeronautical experiment.

Now may be as good a time and place as any to make certain that the reader gains no wrong impression about the writer's intentions. Much has already been written, and more will follow, in praise of aeronautical pioneering of men who preceded Orville and Wilbur Wright. Notwithstanding, this is not to be taken as detracting by so much as a whit from the brothers who flew at Kitty Hawk.

To the Wrights belong the laurels. Nothing which could be written here would change that fact. In the struggle to achieve controlled, heavier-than-air, powered flight, by their own efforts they succeeded where all others had failed. Each failure, each faltering step forward by their predecessors, though, had made more certain the coming of a day when history could be made in the air above the sands of Kitty Hawk.

John Stringfellow, born in England in 1799, became a prosperous manufacturer of carriages, bobbins, and lacemaking machinery. He had the active sort of mind which could be aroused when challenged by something new and difficult. For him the challenge was building a light-weight steam engine to power the invention of William S. Henson—a monoplane aircraft with two six-bladed propellers.

This Stringfellow-Henson effort is noteworthy, because the latter had patented his "aeroplane," and sought, with visible lack of success, to sell £2,000 worth of stock in the Aerial Steam Transit Company, which was to build and operate his machines. This was in 1843. With failure both of the stock sale and a scale model, Henson lost interest, and, in 1847, he sought his further fortune in Texas.

Stringfellow, to the contrary, continued his work on the problems. He improved the steam engine, and built a new model with a 10-foot wing span. With engine and fuel, the total weight was under nine pounds. Some writers credit this as being the first practically powered airplane model capable of approaching continuous and directed flight. At any rate, the model did become airborne, and, in 1848, it made its best effort, a flight of 120 feet; which was approximately the same distance Orville Wright achieved on the first of the four man-carrying flights of the Wright Flyer on December 17, 1903. Thereafter, Stringfellow's work was sporadic, and amounted to little. In 1868, he exhibited a model of a triplane at the Crystal Palace exhibition, and, for the steam engine which powered it, he received a £100 prize.

If the 19th Century deserves characterization as a time of aeronautical invention—most of it unsuccessful—the year 1866, one might say, marks the beginning of a period of research and experiment in aeronautics. It was then that the Aeronautical Society of Great Britain was formed, and the first meeting was memorable for the presentation of a paper by Francis H. Wenham. An engineer, Wenham had studied carefully the flight of birds, and he is credited with having contributed much to an understanding of the technical problems barring the way to successful flight.

Although much of Wenham's work was theoretical, he was more than a mere theorist, and performed considerable experimental work with wing surfaces to determine the connection between velocity and pressure. In passing, mention probably should be made also of F. W. Breary, who, as secretary, kept the society going for 30 years of fat and lean; and also of Thomas Moy, whose theorizing was far more sound than the steam-powered models he was constantly building.

H. F. Phillips was another of the experimenters who contributed importantly to the advance of aeronautics. As a result of painstaking work performed on air foils "in artificial currents of air, produced by induction from a steam jet in a wooden trunk or conduit" Phillips, in 1884, patented a whole series of curved wing shapes for airplanes. These, in the main, borrowed the concave lower surfaces and the convex upper surfaces of a bird's wings, and their form was due to data produced in what was one of the first wind tunnels.

In France, too, aeronautical interest heightened as the Century moved into its last quarter. Alphonse Pénaud (1850–80) was among the most brilliant of the pre-Wright experimenters. He built many models, including one powered by a rubber-band motor, which flew 131 feet. In 1876, he undertook construction of a two-passenger airplane weighing 2,600 pounds. The elliptical wing was to be cambered and with a slight dihedral. The trailing edge of the wing was to be movable (some refer to this feature as being the first appearance of the aileron). The rudder and elevator were to be interconnected, and controlled by a single lever. A speed of 60 miles per hour was calculated, provided a suitably light engine could be found. Pénaud was almost 30 years ahead of his time, as far as light engine requirements were concerned. Too, he was virtually penniless and in poor health. At the age of 30, he committed suicide. If an adequate engine had been available, if he had kept his health, if he could possibly have attracted financial support . . . if, if, if.

By anything approaching chronological standards, the names of Lilienthal, Pilcher and Chanute should be appearing now, and Langley's name, too. These men, who by their work did so much to advance the art and science of aeronautics, will be subjects of following chapters.

Clément Ader, a wealthy French engineer who had prospered with the development of the telephone, spent more than 25 years—and some $120,000—seeking to perfect a flying machine. After his first effort, an ornithopter, proved a failure, Ader spent years studying the flight of birds. In 1886, he built a second machine, called "Eole," with fixed batlike wings, and a four-bladed propeller powered by a steam engine. Weighing 650 pounds, and with a wing span of 46 feet, it was smashed at the end of its first test. Whether it actually flew, as two witnesses declared, was never certain.

In 1891, a third machine, with 54-foot wing span, was reported also to have flown. This winged vehicle showed sufficient promise to cause the French War Ministry to advance funds for construction of his fourth machine. This last, his second "Avion," was powered by two 20-hp. steam engines. In 1897, trials were conducted, with Ader piloting his machine around a 1,600-meter track. The test, like those of so many other hopefuls, before and after, ended in disaster.

Ader was convinced he had flown. So were several observers, although a large number of witnesses were equally sure he had not. Whether he actually flew, or only managed a few hops, really is beside the point. Ader's flying machines were uncontrollable, and hardly to be considered adequate for sustained flight.

His efforts, gallant though they were, lacked even the shaky foundation of aerodynamic knowledge of those who had preceded him. Ader did, nevertheless, succeed in harnessing engines to an air frame, engines which were powerful enough to provide sufficient thrust for flight. If it had been provided with adequate controls, if it had possessed greater stability, Ader's "Avion" might well have qualified as being "capable of flight" . . . if, if, if.

The aeronautical experiments of Thomas Edison, which began in 1880, deserve brief mention, not so much for their value, but rather because they were conducted by a man whose inventions included the incandescent light bulb and the phonograph. Most of Edison's work had to do with the lifting power of propellers, and apparently he convinced himself that there was little future in aeronautics. However, by 1903, only months ahead of the first powered flights by the Wrights, Edison had decided that "the flying machine is bound to come, but it will take some time at the rate we are progressing now."

Finally, for this chapter, comes Sir Hiram Maxim, inventor of a machine gun, a gun silencer and numerous other profitable items. Once he had turned his vigorous mind to aeronautics, he quickly acquainted himself with the state of the art and, as he later wrote, discarded the existing literature as being the product of "professional mathematicians, who have led themselves to believe that all problems connected with mundane life are susceptible of solution by the use of mathematical formulae; providing, of course, that the number of characters employed are numerous enough."

Though Sir Hiram may have had contempt for the theoreticians, he prefaced his aircraft construction efforts by painstaking experiment, using both a wind tunnel and a whirling arm apparatus similar to that employed by Professor Samuel P. Langley. In 1889, he filed patent specifications for his flying machine, and, in 1893, began construction of a full-scale prototype.

The Maxim airplane was a veritable behemoth, with some 4,000 square feet of wing surface. It was powered by two steam engines developing more than 300 horsepower and Sir Hiram proposed to use the steel-tubing framework of his aircraft as a condenser for the power plant, thus cutting down on the weight of water required for steam. In weight, the Maxim machine was heavier than 2½ tons, including fuel and a crew of three.

Sir Hiram had no ambitions for immediate free flight, certainly not until wing lift and the thrust of the propellers had been carefully measured. To accomplish this, he constructed a captive-track arrangement, along which the aircraft could be operated under power. On the last of several runs down the track, a rear axletree broke, and it was necessary to throttle down to avoid a total smashup. According to the Maxim calculations, lift totaling 10,000 pounds had been produced, more than enough to sustain flight. If his machine hadn't been tethered, if it had been equipped with more perfect controls, if Sir Hiram had continued his work . . . if, if, if.

Within the course of the 19th Century, aeronautics had been transformed from the pursuit of visionaries to a goal attainable by talented, practical men. The laws of aerodynamics were as yet imperfectly understood, but at least there had developed a broad awareness of definite ways how not to attempt to fly. Power plants, if not yet suitable, were being improved rapidly. No one could yet establish a date when success would finally come, but, in retrospect, it is certain that such predictions of ultimate accomplishment as were heard were soundly based.

# 3/ THE BIRD MEN

*Our knowledge is a torch of smoky pine*
*That lights the pathway but one step ahead*
*Across a void of mystery and dread.*
*George Santayana*

*"With each advent of spring, when the air is alive with innumerable happy creatures; when the storks on their arrival at their old northern resorts fold up their imposing flying apparatus which has carried them thousands of miles, lay back their heads and announce their arrival by joyously rattling their beaks; when the swallows have made their entry and hurry through our streets and pass our windows in sailing flight; when the lark appears as a dot in the ether and manifests its joy of existence by its song; then a certain desire takes possession of man. He longs to soar upward and to glide, free as the bird, over smiling fields, leafy woods and mirrored lakes, and so enjoy the varying landscape as fully as only a bird can do."*

The man who wrote these words was Otto Lilienthal, a German engineer who has been called, with considerable justice, "the father of glider experiments." It is about him, his brother, Gustav, and others who struggled during the last half of the 19th century to wrest the secret of soaring flight from the birds, that this chapter is concerned. While others were attempting prematurely to apply power to the machines they proposed to fly, these men became immersed in more basic problems.

First, after Sir George Cayley (*see Chapter II*), comes Jean-Marie Le Bris, a French sea captain, whose aerial experiments in Brittany a hundred years ago were spectacular indeed; especially if the reader be inclined to accept uncritically the fact that his successful exploits invariably were without benefit of impartial witnesses. With equal certainty, his efforts ended in disaster when performed in the presence of several persons. The Le Bris story, regardless of the mixture of fact and fantasy, has become so firmly fixed in the history of aeronautics that it requires inclusion at this point.

Le Bris, according to Chanute (who quoted de la Landelle), gained inspiration and knowledge during his sea voyages by observing the soaring flight of the albatross. After he had killed one and studied it, he took its wing and exposed it to the breeze. Then, we are told, the sea captain exclaimed: "And lo! in spite of me it drew forward into the wind; notwithstanding my resistance it tended to rise. Thus I had discovered the secret of the bird! I comprehended the whole mystery of flight."

In 1854 or '55, he built an artificial albatross of wood and cloth with a boat-like body. Its wing had a span of about 50 feet. To get into the air, Le Bris hitched his flyer to the back of a horse-drawn cart, and away they went down the road into the face of a 12-mile wind. Up soared his albatross to a height of 300 feet, and LeBris yanked at the slip-knot which would release the tow rope.

Unfortunately, it tangled around the driver of the cart and hauled him into the air. Hearing the howls which followed, Le Bris coolly manipulated the controls and lowered his passenger to earth, then brought his machine down for a landing that resulted in damage to the albatross, but not to its inventor. Later, Le Bris elevated his machine over a quarry for takeoff, and on this try broke a leg, in addition to smashing the glider. In 1867, a public subscription was raised to finance his work, which hereafter was little more than experimentation with kites; just as, some hard-headed critic might write, had been the case with his initial ventures.

As a small boy, soon to be orphaned, Otto Lilienthal and his brother used to stalk the stork on the peaceful meadows near their German home. Otto's alert mind pondered the fact that often the ungainly bird would hop *towards* them when disturbed, until sufficiently lifted by the force of its flapping wings. "Even at that time it became obvious," his brother Gustav later wrote, "that rising against the wind must be easier than with the wind, because without some compelling cause the shy bird would not advance towards us."

From those days, prior to 1860, until his tragic death in '96, Otto Lilienthal was obsessed with the urge "not to rest until we have attained to a perfect conception of the problem of flight." As teenagers, he and Gustav constructed "flying machines," first with wings each measuring 6 by 3 feet, and then 9 by 3 feet; but, for the time, they forgot the lesson of the stork and sought to fly in a perfect calm. Gustav's role throughout was that of the follower and the chronicler; there is little evidence of the "oneness" which characterized the Brothers Wright, who were to be so influenced by learning of Lilienthal's work.

Experiments with machine number three were interrupted by the Franco-Prussian War of 1870, but quickly resumed thereafter. Otto was seeking to develop an ornithopter, a flapping-wing mechanism that would sustain man in flight, but, as his systematic work progressed, he did much to evolve a semblance of order from the chaos of information and misinformation which comprised the sum of aeronautical knowledge of the day.

From 1871 to 1891, in addition to work with ornithopter models, Otto applied himself to speculation and calculation of aerodynamic principles. Most of his beliefs came from studies of bird flight, but he also employed a "whirling machine," not unlike that used by Langley in his experimentations. Perhaps independently of Phillips (*see Chapter II*) Lilienthal recognized the superior lifting qualities of a curved wing with thickened leading edge, over a flat plate. With the principle established to his satisfaction, both by theory and experiment, Otto concluded a discussion of the matter in 1889 by observing that "we also find that Nature utilizes the advantage of curved wings even in the vegetable kingdom, by providing the seeds of certain plants with slightly curved wings, so as to enable them to sail along in the wind."

In 1891, Lilienthal decided to compare the actual lifting power of larger curved surfaces with the values he and his brother had derived from their work with model wing shapes. The result, in the following years, was development of a series of gliders with fixed wings, and with them Otto made some 2,000 flights, many from an artificial hill about 50 feet high which he had had built on the plains near Berlin. At first, he used monoplane gliders, but later he built biplanes, and appeared to favor this design.

Otto Lilienthal achieved a measure of stability and control during these gliding flights by moving his weight backwards or forwards or from side to side, as was required. He reported that, after a time, his movements became instinctive and automatic, much as a man, easily and without conscious effort, maintains the balance of his bicycle. Otto's best glides were as long as 1,200 feet.

In 1896, it was felt further improvement in the gliding results could not be attained, and the Lilienthal brothers undertook construction of a machine with flapping wings, powered by a carbonic-acid motor. On August 9, 1896, while testing this device as a fixed-wing glider and with a new rudder, Otto lost control. In the resulting crash, from a height of about 50 feet, he was fatally injured.

Otto Lilienthal differed from some of his contemporaries and earlier experimenters; he recognized that his machines were the means, not the end. Always ready to make use of ideas or information from outside sources, he nonetheless felt there was too much theorizing, "on paper, in projects, and in aeronautical papers and in discussions." He performed much research into the problems of flight, but he realized also that in the air itself were to be found many answers. His work represented an especially happy mating of the theoretical and experimental approaches to the problem.

Regarded as one of the greatest of the early pioneers of flight, Otto Lilienthal had demonstrated beyond doubt the superiority of curved airfoils over flat surfaces, and also had reduced the art of gliding to actual practice. Perhaps most importantly, by his accomplishments he aroused widespread enthusiasm among others. Among these were Percy Pilcher and Octave Chanute. Also, there were Orville and Wilbur Wright.

Well might all who aspired to fly heed Lilienthal's counsel: "The method which is to lead to practical flight must be capable of development, be its beginning ever so primitive, and by it we must be afforded an opportunity of really skimming through the air, by which we may gain experience as to the stability of flight, the action of the wind, and safe landing, in order, by continued development, gradually to approach permanent free flight. Perfection cannot be forced immediately. It is because inventors require too much from their constructions that the positive results are so little. . . . Whoever loses sight of healthy development by continually increased experience, will never attain anything in this sphere."

Percy S. Pilcher, a young Englishman not yet 30 years old, was a practicing engineer with a naval background. In the middle '90s, having done some work for Sir Hiram Maxim, he became interested in gliders, and built his first, the "Bat," which was unsuccessful. In 1895, he visited Lilienthal in Germany and was permitted to make several flights in one of Lilienthal's biplane gliders.

For a time, Pilcher continued to favor the monoplane principle because he felt a biplane would be "very difficult to handle in bad weather." He rebuilt the "Bat," and got better results. In 1896, following further experimentation with two new machines, the "Beetle" and the "Gull," he built his fourth and most successful glider, the "Hawk." Its frame work was bamboo, except for two wooden spars, and its wing surface was 180 square feet. It had a landing gear, including wheels. In his "Hawk," Pilcher made numerous gliding flights during the next two years, including one of 750 feet.

Encouraged by his progress, Pilcher felt ready to attempt powered flight. He calculated that an engine of three—or, at most, four—horsepower would suffice. "An engine said to give one horsepower, and to weigh but 15 pounds, was it is true, reported to be in existence in America; but every endeavor to trace it was effectively baffled," Pilcher wrote, and so, in 1898, he designed and commenced construction of his own engine. He calculated it would weigh 44 pounds, including the propeller, and that it would provide 4 horsepower. It is believed he planned to use the engine in a new machine, a triplane.

On September 30, 1899, Pilcher had promised to give a gliding demonstration. The day was rainy, and he decided to use his "Hawk," taking off from level ground after being towed by horses, à la Le Bris. On his first attempt, the tow rope broke. On a second try, he had risen to a height of 30 feet when a guy-wire snapped and the machine crashed. The next day, the 34-year-old Pilcher died from his injuries. Although he failed to make contributions of the magnitude of Lilienthal, Pilcher's efforts strengthened a growing belief that controlled heavier-than-air flight was possible and that it soon would be realized.

Accounts by the historians concerning the early aeronautical accomplishments of John J. Montgomery, Santa Clara (Calif.) College professor, range as widely as the unabashed admiration and open skepticism they variously show. Certain it is that, in 1893, Montgomery's comments at the Third International Conference on Aerial Navigation in Chicago showed an awareness of air flows around, and pressures on, wings which previously had been only imperfectly understood. Less clear is how successful were Montgomery's experiments, beginning in 1883. First he built an ornithopter, with results that were uncertain. Next he constructed three gliders which, according to his own account in 1909, demonstrated exactly the necessity for curved wing surfaces.

After the turn of the century, having continued his work studying problems of equilibrium and control, Montgomery built several man-carrying gliders which were lofted into the sky by balloons, and then were cut loose. Even if the California professor's earlier work were unjustly discounted to zero worth, the acrobatic exploits in public by his team of three flyers, beginning in 1905, would make memory of the Montgomery name deserved.

Perhaps their antics, including a corkscrew descent and side somersaults, may have been foolhardy, but it would appear that the troubles which followed were due to causes other than inherent weaknesses of the Montgomery gliders. In 1905, one of the pilots was killed when a guy rope from the "mother balloon" became snagged around one of the glider wings at the moment of release. In 1906, the great earthquake which hit San Francisco caused Montgomery to interrupt his experiment and displays until 1911. In that year, according to *American Aeronautics*, while he was making a flight himself, "a little whirlwind caught the machine and dashed it, head on, to the ground; Prof. Montgomery landed on his head and right hip." At first he did not believe himself seriously hurt. Soon after he complained of pain and died.

For Octave Chanute, aeronautics was little more than an avocation, a sort of talking hobby, until he reached his middle 60s. He was a Parisian who had been brought to America at the age of six. Trained as a civil engineer, he achieved substantial fortune and a deserved reputation; in 1891, he was honored by being chosen president of the American Society of Civil Engineers. He won honors for designing a bridge at St. Charles, Mo., the first to span the Missouri. He designed and superintended construction of the Union Stockyards in Chicago. He was a builder of railroads in the Middle West. Here was a man who could do things, big and new—do them well.

Until the 90s, Chanute's aeronautical activities were largely confined to gathering, as he later wrote, "from time to time such information as was to be found on the subject." In 1893, he gave stature to the cause when, as chairman of the Third International Conference on Aerial Navigation in Chicago, he succeeded in programming more than two score learned papers on as many aspects of the aeronautical art. The year following, in addition to publishing the proceedings of the congress, Chanute brought out "Progress in Flying Machines," a volume of more than 100,000 words, which told with remarkable clarity, completeness and authority, the history of aviation to that time.

Notwithstanding, Chanute—now possessing the freedom of retirement together with the vigor of a man much younger than his years—was not content with such sedentary aeronautical activity. Admittedly, Chanute was stirred by the work of others because, in 1900, he looked back and wrote: "It was only after Lilienthal had shown that such an adventure was feasible that courage was gathered to experiment with full-sized machines carrying a man through the air." Always eager to encourage others towards the goal, and to aid by sharing his knowledge, he had a way of noting in a manner most gentle what he thought to be flaws in the work of another.

Prior to Lilienthal's death in 1896, Chanute had undertaken construction of a glider along the lines of the German design, but with an important difference. Where Lilienthal sought to maintain equilibrium in flight by shifting the weight of his body, Chanute proposed, instead, to provide a mechanism that would automatically provide the desired stability and control by moving the wings.

In 1896 and 1897, Chanute made some 2,000 gliding flights along the shores of Lake Michigan, with the aid of a couple of younger enthusiast-employes including A. M. Herring—who had made flights in 1894 in a Lilienthal-type glider and in 1895 had worked briefly for Prof. Samuel P. Langley (*see Chapter IV*). In later years, Herring would become briefly associated with Glenn Curtiss, and would earn the dislike of the Wright Brothers. In addition to the Lilienthal-type glider, the Chanute group used, at first, a six-winged machine, with five plane surfaces stacked one above the other, and the sixth trailing behind. Neither model provided results that were especially encouraging. So Chanute moved to a third design.

After some experimentation, and the elimination of surfaces believed to be unnecessary, this last glider assumed the biplane form which was to be generally employed in aircraft even up to as recently as the 1920s and '30s. What Chanute had done was to transfer to the field of aeronautics the strut and diagonal wire bracing of the Pratt truss, with which he had been acquainted as a civil engineer.

In all, five man-carrying gliders were flown from the sand dunes near the Chanute camp. His own best distance was 359 feet; Herring is credited with having flown nearly three times as far. Chanute published reports of this work in 1897, in the *Journal* of the Western Society of Engineers and in the *Aeronautical Annual.* He judged the experiments to have been promising, and invited "other experimenters to improve upon our practice." The invitation remained unaccepted until March, 1900, when, Chanute later recalled, "Wilbur Wright wrote to me, making inquiries as to the construction of the machine, materials to be used, the best place to experiment, etc. He said that he had notions of his own that he wanted to try, and knew of no better way of spending his vacation. All that information was gladly furnished."

The interchange of letters marked the beginning of a warm and lasting friendship between Octave Chanute on the one hand and Wilbur and Orville Wright on the other. Each year through 1903, as the Wrights went to Kitty Hawk, Chanute visited them at their camp, giving encouragement and counsel. Except for delays due to mechanical failures, and bitterly cold weather, for which he had no liking, Chanute might have seen the first successful flight—because he was at the Wright camp in November of 1903.

During the years from '03 until the Wrights had surely won international recognition in 1908, Chanute was always close. He was a not infrequent visitor, and the flow of correspondence between him and the Wrights was heavy. The intimate relationship, sometimes resembling on Chanute's part the fondly proud attitude of a foster parent, continued until his death in November, 1910. In the latter years, the friendship was tried and tested by several relatively minor differences in point of view, but, on both sides, there was evident an earnest desire to keep firm the bonds of mutual friendship and understanding.

There is no question that the Wrights gained much from Octave Chanute, in guidance and in inspiration. Equally, they gave much in return, including the most precious gift of all, performance that matched perfectly his hope and belief that the goal of the useful airplane could be reached.

# 4/ SAMUEL P. LANGLEY

*". . . This unlooked for claim*
*At the first hearing, for a moment took*
*More hope out of his life than he supposed*
*That any old man could have lost."*
*Wordsworth*

Samuel P. Langley was a man of science, courage, and unflagging perseverance. His story is tragic and peculiarly American.

Langley had many talents. When the Civil War interfered with his career as an architect in Chicago, he returned to Boston to become an assistant at the Harvard Observatory. In 1866, he was named assistant professor of mathematics at the Naval Academy at Annapolis. The following year, he became professor of physics and astronomy at the Western University of Pennsylvania (since 1908 the University of Pittsburgh).

For the next 20 years, Langley was concerned principally with matters of astronomy at the University's Allegheny Observatory. By 1886, at the age of 52, he had earned recognition for his contributions to the science. That year marked the beginning of his researches in aerodynamics. His interest in the subject, at least at first, was not so much to improve upon the practicalities of heavier-than-air flight as to test the validity of one of Newton's laws—that the resistance of a plane surface to the air varies as the square of the sine of its angle of incidence.

For his experiments, Langley needed adequate equipment and necessary funds. These were forthcoming from William Thaw, Pittsburgh millionaire. The apparatus Langley had built to his specifications was a whirling table, with arms 30 feet long. In his own words, it was "of unprecedented size, mounted in the open air and driven round by a steam engine, so that the end of its revolving arm swept through a circumference of 200 feet at all speeds up to 70 miles an hour."

Langley got his whirling table operating in 1887. Brass plates, attached to the end of one of the arms, were whirled around at various speeds and varying angles of inclination. A spring-and-scale attachment provided measurements. He decided that the curved surfaces, favored by Lilienthal, "are in some degree more efficient" than flat plates, but only slightly so.

Langley came to the conclusion, as his experiments continued, that air resistance was but 1/20th that indicated by Newton. He believed, also, that less power would be required to support a thin plane surface in the air at high speed than at low speed. He calculated that one horsepower, rightly applied, could sustain more than 200 pounds in the air at express-train speed.

By this enunciation of "Langley's Law" (and its corollary: "so far as the mere power to sustain heavier-than-air bodies in the air by mechanical flight goes, such mechanical flight is possible with engines we now possess, since effective steam engines have lately been built weighing less than 10 pounds to 1 horsepower") he gave great encouragement to all who sought to develop the airplane.

The fact that Langley's Law was in error because it failed to take due account of the rise in drag—aeronautical pioneers of his day would have called it "drift"—as speed increased, is, paradoxically, beside the point. After all, at the low speeds of the first airplanes, the drag forces would be relatively small. What *is* important was that here was a man who knew what he was talking about, saying that what previously had seemed impossible to all but the dreamers was—actually—entirely possible!

In 1889, Dr. Langley went to The Smithsonian Institution as assistant secretary. Soon after, he became secretary, and, beginning in 1891, his aerodynamic findings were published by The Smithsonian, and were widely read.

In 1906, Wilbur Wright wrote a letter to Chanute, in which he recalled that "the knowledge that the head of the most prominent scientific institution of America believed in the possibility of human flight was one of the influences that led us to undertake the preliminary investigation that preceded our active work."

At The Smithsonian, the duties of operating head of the institution were many and complex, but still Dr. Langley was encouraged to find time for further study and experiment, both in aeronautics and astronomy. His readings acquainted him with the work of Pénaud (*see Chapter II*), and led to construction of a small airplane model, powered by a rubber band. It was similar to one flown for 13 seconds by the French experimenter, but Langley's replica could manage flight for hardly half that brief time.

In all, Langley had some two-score rubber-powered models made. He also directed experiments with models using other kinds of power plants, including tiny engines driven by steam, hot water under pressure, compressed air, gas, electricity, carbonic acid, and gunpowder. He referred to this period as one of "fruitless experiment in the construction of models supplied with various motors, subsequent to, and on a larger scale indeed, than the toy-like ones of india rubber, but not even so efficient as those had been, since they had never procured a single flight."

At the same time, Langley had been pondering the ability of birds to soar indefinitely, seemingly without effort. In April, 1893, he read a paper, "The Internal Work of the Wind," to the National Academy of Sciences, and, in August of the same year, to the International Conference on Aerial Navigation in Chicago.

In brief, he observed that no satisfactory mechanical explanation had been offered to explain the ability of birds to soar, and then went on to offer his own. It was to the effect that the wind was never "approximately uniform, but variable and irregular in its movements beyond anything which had been anticipated." He felt "there might be a potentiality of what may be called 'internal work' in the wind," which could be utilized—if man could only learn how—not only to "keep an inert body from falling, but cause it to rise," and that this power probably was the secret of the soaring birds.

Langley concluded: "The final application of these principles to the art of aerodynamics seems, then, to be, that while it is not likely that the perfected aerodrome [*his name for an airplane*] will ever be able to dispense altogether with the ability to rely at intervals on some internal source of power, it will not be indispensable that this aerodrome of the future shall, in order to go any distance—even to circumnavigate the globe without alighting—need carry a weight of fuel which would enable it to perform this journey under conditions analogous to those of a steamship, but that the fuel and weight need only be such as to enable it to take care of itself in exceptional moments of calm."

Here again, one finds Dr. Langley arriving at an approximation surprisingly close to the right answer, even though the numbers he was adding for his total may have been individually incorrect. Thermals . . . internal work of the wind . . . shifting air currents . . . whatever the cause, sailplanes have been flown more than 500 miles nonstop, and higher than 40,000 feet, without benefit of engines!

In 1893, Dr. Langley began what was perhaps his most intensive and fruitful period of aeronautical activity. He pondered the problems of airframe design and construction. He studied propellers, using a pendulum arrangement to test their efficiency. He gave attention to such matters as stability and control.

Because of growing administrative responsibilities and, no less, because he was a man who worked with his head rather than his hands, Dr. Langley throughout his aerodynamic experiments had to rely upon the skill of others. Fortunately, as the operating head of The Smithsonian, he could call upon the talents of skilled carpenters, precision machinists, and inventive instrument makers. When it came to development of his small engines, he was aided by a physicist, Dr. Carl Barus. At various times, E. C. Huffaker and A. M. Herring, two aeronautical experimenters who had worked with Chanute, served as assistants, and there were others, accomplished in their own specialty, who also gave a helping hand.

Before he could hope to launch a successful model into the air, he needed an engine which in power and in lightness would be suitable for his tiny craft. Langley chose steam as offering the greatest possibilities, and, during 1893–96, he directed a systematic program to develop and perfect the elements of such an engine.

Consider the problem, in light of the metallurgical art 70 years ago, of designing and constructing a steam engine which would produce 1 horsepower or more, and yet weigh less than 7 pounds. An essential part, the fire-grate, could weigh only a few ounces. To stay within this weight limitation, which at first seemed impossible, Langley adapted the aeolipile of Hero—50 years later it would serve again as an inspiration, this time to the developers of the turbojet engine—to serve as the burner. "Construction of this small aeolipile was an epoch in the history of the aerodrome," Langley observed, with some justifiable pride.

So it was a step by step progression towards the still distant day, when one of Dr. Langley's models would rise above a long succession of failures that would have frustrated a man of lesser determination. Even before the end of 1893, field trials were being carried on from a houseboat moored at Chopawamsic Island on the Potomac River, near Quantico, Virginia.

The model size had grown to 9.1 pounds "flying weight," with a pair of engines providing 0.4 horsepower, but the pattern of failure remained unbroken. The launching mechanism (forerunner of the apparatus used in 1903) was mounted on top of the houseboat, and frequently was troublesome. The weather seldom was suitable for a flight attempt; it had to be almost flat calm before the experimenters would risk a launching of one of the fragile models. More often than not, the engines were out of order when everything else was set for a trial.

During 1894 the story was essentially the same. Two models were being used, a modified Number 4 weighing 14.5 pounds when ready for flight, and Number 5, weighing 22 pounds in the same ready condition. On October 6 of that year, Number 5 was launched successfully, climbed at an angle of about 60 degrees, flew about 35 feet, and slid backward into the water . . . all within 3 seconds.

October 27, during a launch of Number 4, a guy wire caught on the launching car; the same day, it was observed that the wings of Number 5 "visibly pocketed" during a 3½-second flight. On November 21, "a piece flew out of the port propeller" of Number 5, and it plunged "head downward into the water at a distance of 30 feet." Finally, for the year, the flight of Number 5 on December 8 "was so short that it was as unsatisfactory as before."

"These trials gave a very vivid object lesson of what had already been anticipated," Dr. Langley wrote with no trace of discouragement, "that the difficulties of actual flight would probably lie even more in obtaining exact balance than in the first and more obvious difficulty of obtaining the mere engine power to sustain a machine in the air."

In 1895, it was decided that two pairs of wings, in tandem like a dragonfly's, would be employed. For control, a Pénaud-type tail was specified. It consisted of a horizontal stabilizer and a vertical fin. Langley felt that "this not only added to the stability of the aerodrome, but also made it possible, without any alteration in the plan of the frame, to bring the center of pressure into the proper position relative to the center of gravity."

May 6, 1896, Dr. Alexander Graham Bell was present for trials of Models Numbers 5 and 6, weighing about 26 pounds each. The first of these to be launched was Model Number 6, but "the guy-wire uniting the wings having apparently caught on one of the fixed wooden strips which held the wings down, the left wing was broken."

Next came a launch of Number 5. Off it went, to remain airborne for 1 minute, 20 seconds, during which it flew some 3,000 feet, reaching a height estimated between 70 and 100 feet.

The same day, Number 5 made a second flight of 2,300 feet, and, in November, 1896, Number 6 flew a distance of 4,200 feet at about 30 miles per hour. "Just what these flights meant to Mr. Langley can be readily understood. They meant success!" So wrote his enthusiastic assistant, Charles M. Manly, who then continued: "For the first time in the history of the world, a device produced by man had actually flown through the air, and had preserved its equilibrium without the aid of a guiding human intelligence."

Dr. Langley, writing in *McClure's* Magazine for June, 1897, stated: "I have now brought to a close the portion of the work which seemed to be specially mine—the demonstration of the practicability of mechanical flight—and for the next stage, which is the commercial and practical development of the idea, it is probable that the world may look to others."

Except for an essentially political development the following year, it is possible Dr. Langley might have withstood the longing to take the final step toward actually transporting a human being through the air. He was in his mid-sixties; the administrative responsibilities he carried as secretary of The Smithsonian were, if anything, continuing to grow in weight and multiplicity. Ten years of intensive effort had sapped his strength; his physician counseled that a resumption of similarly concentrated thought and vigorous effort would shorten materially his life.

Finally, the problems involved in scaling up to man-carrying size an airplane and its engine reflecting the qualities of the successful models would be formidable. At the least, they would equal those which previously had proved so difficult.

The political development was war with Spain, and the invitation to Dr. Langley to construct a flying machine with possibilities as a weapon of war was at the direction of President McKinley. Langley, in a memorandum attached to his letter of acceptance of December 12, 1898, claimed "an exclusive right of property in the results of the experiments in aerodromics which would remain his unqualifiedly." He added that he was glad to place these results, without charge, at the service of the Army for construction of the airplane "which seems to me to be of National utility." He estimated that the cost of the work would be "within the sum of $50,000."

In both his letter of acceptance and the attached memorandum, Langley emphasized that the project was to be carried forward in "privacy." Had this been possible, it is more than likely that ridicule and abuse which later were his lot in heart-breaking quantities might not have been forthcoming.

Prior to committing himself to the undertaking, Dr. Langley had made a search for a reliable builder who could construct a gasoline engine of not less than 12 horsepower, weighing not more than 100 pounds. Such a powerplant, he felt, was much to be preferred to a steam engine of equal power, but so fragile as to be unreliable. A contract was let with S. M. Balzar of New York for two engines with delivery to be made not later than February 28, 1899.

In June, 1898, Dr. Langley enlisted the aid of his assistant, Mr. Manly, a Cornell University graduate, to take charge of the technical aspects of designing a sturdy, full-scale airframe. His choice hardly could have been more fortunate; in addition to possessing the engineering background required for the job, Manly was to prove himself something of a genius when it came to powerplant design.

First, Manly undertook an analysis of the structures of the small models, and found that the essentially cut-and-try methods used in their construction had resulted in a situation where "most of the parts were working under stresses generally far above the elastic limit of the materials, and, in many cases, the ultimate breaking strength was closely approached." The business of scaling up was made substantially more difficult, of course, by the "law of the cube," with weight increasing as the cube, while the supporting surfaces increased only as the square.

During 1899, preliminary work was performed in designing and constructing the frame of the man-carrying airplane. At the same time, the engine manufacturer continued efforts to make good belatedly on his already overdue engine contract. During this period, the models used in 1896 were strengthened and employed for further experimental flights at Chopawamsic Island on the Potomac.

*This same year, 1899, the Hague Peace Conference went on record to the effect that aircraft, present or projected, would not by international law be permitted to take a combatant part in war. The discharge of projectiles or explosives from the air was solemnly prohibited; air vehicles were to be limited in use to reconnaissance or equally passive roles.*

As before, successful flights were few. Always there was trouble of some kind. The Langley venture was ever bedevilled by one difficulty which the Wrights would escape; the construction and the launching of his models—this applies, no less, to the man-carrying machine—were left, by necessity, to hired hands.

Referring to a mishap July 28, 1899, Manly would later write that it emphasized "the fact that even the best workmen, who have had several years of experience, cannot be relied on in anything which required that everything be done *exactly right* and not *nearly right*." Again, with reference to a smashup on August 1 of the same year, he would observe, with feeling, that "the disaster was entirely due to the carelessness of one of the workmen in tightening one of the wires, a further example of the extreme heedlessness of workmen, even in the most important details, which concern the very existence of the machine."

Despite troubles, major and minor, work continued. A new, larger houseboat was made ready for the day when the full-sized airplane could be flown. Constructed at large cost, it measured 40 by 60 feet, and provided sleeping quarters for a crew of eight workmen, as well as an on-the-spot workshop, and storage space for the aircraft, spare wings, and the like. Atop the houseboat was a turntable weighing some 15 tons, which incorporated a spring catapult and permitted heading the airplane into the wind for launching. The launching gear was 80 feet long.

Because, biplane design would provide real advantages structurally over Langley's dragon-fly arrangement, further tests were conducted. It was decided, however, that the aerodynamic advantages of the tandem wings outweighed the structural benefits which accrued from biplane positioning.

Propeller testing also was carried on, with a special hand car being used along a straight stretch of railroad track near Mount Holly, N.J. Supervision of the tests, as usual, had to be entrusted by Dr. Langley to others. The project was a failure.

In May of 1900, more than a year after Balzar had agreed to deliver the engines, Manly went to New York and, after several weeks with the manufacturer, he decided there was no immediate hope of making the New York design work. Certainly, Balzar had made a determined try; according to Manly, he spent something like $10,000 in actual wages over and above the contract price, to say nothing of shop costs, but the Langley airplane would have been earthbound indefinitely unless some other power-plant source could be found.

That summer, Manly accompanied Dr. Langley to Europe to spend six weeks in a canvass of motor makers in hope of finding someone who could and would produce engines of the desired power and weight. "Everywhere the builders," Manly reported, "said that they did not care to undertake the work, and that they did not consider it possible to construct an engine of 12 hp. weighing less than 220 to 230 pounds, or that, if they had thought it possible, they would already have built it, as they had numerous inquiries for such engines, and also wanted them for their own use."

So, to condense the story, Manly returned to America to design and build a 5-cylinder, 4-cycle radial engine which, in weight and performance, was little short of revolutionary. What he managed to do was to construct a power plant which, with 20 pounds of cooling water and all accessories, still weighed only 207.47 pounds. Yet it developed a constant load of 52.4 horsepower during three runs of 10 hours each. Among the many interesting parts which Manly designed for the special purposes at hand were the twin flywheels, which were fabricated of cast and machined aluminum with steel, bicycle-type spokes.

Ready for the flight attempt in the summer of 1903, the Langley man-carrying machine measured 48 feet from wing tip to wing tip, and 52 feet from nose to tail. The framework was of steel tubing, and bevel gearing transmitted power from the engine to the two pusher propellers. The wings were covered with cotton percaline, with a total area of 1,040 square feet. Each of the four wings weighed less than 30 pounds. Total weight was 850 pounds, including the pilot.

Considerable effort was devoted to development of a device which would provide "automatic equilibrium." Dr. Langley had suggested several ideas, including one he forwarded when it came to him during a trip to Italy. Manly worked out another method, but it was feared that the rapid acceleration provided by the catapult launching gear might cause the device to malfunction.

Besides, it was reasoned that "the main desideratum was to obtain a flight of the larger machine as soon as possible, and perfection of steering control seemed secondary." So, rather than risk the unpredictable effects resulting from further changes, a Pénaud tail, like that used on the models, was installed, with steering to be provided by an auxiliary rudder which was placed just aft of the propellers.

On July 14, with balancing tests completed, the airplane was loaded aboard the houseboat to be towed down the Potomac some 40 miles to a point opposite Widewater, Va. Certainly, it was expected, the experiments would be completed within four weeks.

Dr. Langley had hoped to launch his airplane privately; he had so stipulated in his agreement with the Army. The Potomac, though, is free, navigable water; thus he should not have been overly surprised by the appearance of a flotilla of boats carrying newspapermen. After all, what he was attempting to do *was* news, win or lose. For three months, the press crews would bob up and down not far from the houseboat, waiting with lessening patience for the big day.

First, before the man-carrying vehicle could be launched, it was felt prudent to make final trials with a quarter-size model. Embodying the design principles of the larger machine, it was the first of the Langley models to be powered by a gasoline engine. Inevitably there were delays; it was not until August 8 that the model was launched, to make a sustained flight of approximately 1,000 feet.

Now, surely, everything was ready for the historic first flight of the big machine. Manly, who had been so successful in designing the engine, volunteered to be the "aviator." His special equipment for the venture included only a life preserver, goggles and tennis shoes.

For almost a month the weather was bad without letup. Finally, on September 3, the weather cleared and the airplane was lifted into place on the launching platform. However, the batteries needed for starting the engine had gone bad, and replacements were no nearer than Washington. Worse, it was accidentally discovered that the continued dampness had all but dissolved the glued joints of the cross ribs of the wings.

Of course, that meant a further delay of weeks. Meantime, the same, all-pervading fog was corroding the last vestiges of sympathy and enthusiasm with which the press corps may have been imbued at the beginning of the death watch. Nor did it help that, once the machine was repaired, the weather, which had been unprecedentedly bad all summer, now managed to become even much worse.

Finally, the day of trial did come—October 7, 1903. Ironically, Dr. Langley was not present; he had been detained in Washington by Smithsonian official business.

The machine was hoisted onto the launching platform. At 12.20 p.m., Manly started the engine and took a final survey of the whole machine. Then he seated himself in the "aviator's car" and grasped the controls.

Let a man who then and for more than 50 years earned his living as a working newspaperman, report what happened. Wrote George Rothwell Brown in his story for the Washington *Post:*

"Manly looked down and smiled. Then his face hardened as he braced himself for the flight, which might have in store for him fame or death. The propeller wheels, a foot from his head, whirred around him 1,000 times to the minute. A man forward fired two skyrockets. There came an answering 'toot, toot' from the tugs. A mechanic stooped, cut the cable holding the catapult; there was a roaring grinding noise—and the Langley airship tumbled over the edge of the house-boat and disappeared in the river, 16 feet below.

"It simply slid into the water like a handful of mortar . . ."

Except for the ducking, Manly was unhurt. Pressed for a statement, he blamed the failure on incorrect balancing of the aircraft. Later, it was determined a part of the launching gear, supposed to fall clear at the moment of takeoff, had fouled, twisting and pulling the airframe down to disaster.

Further examination showed the engine to have been undamaged, and the airframe to be readily repairable. Dr. Langley issued a statement in which he referred to the matter as "one of the large chapter of accidents that beset the initial stages of experiments so novel as the present ones," and reaffirmed confidence of ultimate success.

If another attempt was to be made—Manly offered to try again—there was need for haste. The $50,000 from the Army had long been spent; so had some $20,000 provided by the Smithsonian. The wreck, aboard the houseboat, was towed up the Potomac to Washington.

Here, by mid-November, the Langley machine was restored for another try: but again the weather was bad, worsening day by day.

December 8, even large blocks of floating ice several inches thick failed to change the desperate "now or never" decision to make a final attempt. It was nearly dusk when all was ready.

The official report of the Army, issued January 6, 1904, told this grim eye-witness account:

"The car was set in motion and the propellers revolved rapidly, the engine working perfectly, but there was something wrong with the launching, and a crashing, rending sound, followed by the collapse of the rear wings, showed that the machine had been wrecked in the launching, just how it was impossible for me to see. The fact remains that the rear wings and rudder were wrecked before the machine was free of the ways."

The airplane plummeted into the water directly in front of the houseboat, and Manly had to fight his way out of the submerged wreckage. When he did bob to the surface, he bumped his head into the underside of a large block of ice, but finally he was hauled aboard a row boat and carried to shore.

Until now, there had been a chance for success: but with the Army quick to tell the world that it was not "prepared to make an additional allotment at this time for continuing this work," the floodgates of contumely were immediately opened.

Mark Sullivan, in *Our Times*, recalled some of the more cruel jibes:

*"Here is $100,000 of the people's money wasted on this scientific aerial navigation experiment because some man, perchance a professor wandering in his dreams, was able to impress officers that his scheme had some utility."*

*"Perhaps if Professor Langley had only thought to launch his airship bottom up, it would have gone into the air instead of down into the water."*

*"I don't know how much larger Professor Langley's machine is than its flying model was—about large enough, I think, to require an atmosphere a little denser than the intelligence of one scientist, but not quite so dense as that of two."*

"Yesterday's failure," The Washington *Star* editorial writer commented, "of the Langley aeroplane, it is explained, was due, as in the first case, to a fault of the launching device. The machine was not sent forth into the air sufficiently straight to give it a chance to perform according to schedule. Therefore, as viewed by the inventor and his assistants, the airship is itself all right, but the method of starting it is as yet far from perfect. It is as though a great gun had been made, perfect in its own parts, but incapable of being fired safely because of a defect in the ignition device.

"The public will not be disposed to analyze the failure of the aeroplane very keenly. It will regard the general results. It will not discriminate closely between the machine itself and its launching accessory. It will persist in regarding the launching apparatus as an essential feature of the whole. For without the launching appliance the ship itself is as useless as an unassembled mass of steel and wood and cloth.

"Of course, there is still hope. Hope, indeed, springs eternal in the breast of the seeker for the secret of human flight. But if once a perfect launching device can be secured, there will remain the test of the machine itself, which as yet is unproved. Then when the launching device is so made as to stand all tests, and the machine is safely projected into the air and sustains itself and is brought under control, there will yet remain the even more important question of alighting. It is one thing to leap off a building and to hold the body in the position demanded by theory to ensure a safe descent, but it is another thing to manage to hit the ground with sufficient gentleness. It was an Irish hod carrier who declared that he was never hurt by falling off a scaffold. It was the bringing up at the bottom that broke his ribs."

Prodded by Manly, who was to remain confident of the vehicle's capabilities to his death in 1927, Dr. Langley authorized expenditure of the small sum required for repair of the airframe, and proper care for the undamaged engine. Manly now went further, and sought additional financial backing to continue the work.

Money was forthcoming, Manly later wrote, but with the proviso that arrangements be "made for later commercialization." Though Dr. Langley earlier had sought to protect the rights to his work, he had "never patented anything previously in his life," and, in the light of what had happened, he refused "to consent to capitalize his scientific work."

In 1906 Dr. Langley died, and the press reports now referred to him as the victim of a broken heart.

In 1914, the Langley aircraft—with modifications, and fitted with floats—was flown from the waters of Lake Keuka near Hammondsport, N.Y. The event has been described as prima facie evidence that, except for malfunctions of the launching gear, most certainly Dr. Langley's airplane would have made successful flights in 1903. With equal forthrightness and conviction, it has been described as a fake operation, perpetrated by men who stood to gain financially.

By 1942, fortunately, agreement was reached among the persons most concerned, and yet alive, respecting the changes which had been made to the Langley machine prior to the Hammondsport tests. The Smithsonian observed that "inferences from the comparisons (between the 1903 and 1914 versions) are primarily the province of interested experts . . ." and with that the controversy was officially ended.

Dr. Langley has been likened to a prophet of old who, after 40 years of wandering in the wilderness, was permitted to view the promised land upon which he never set foot. His accomplishments in aeronautics were notable, even though his man-carrying machine failed in 1903.

# 5/ THE WRIGHT BROTHERS SUCCEED

*"Imagination, new and strange*
*In every age, can turn the year;*
*Can shift the poles and lightly change*
*The mood of men, the world's career."*
*John Davidson*

On December 14, 1903, the Wright Flyer was ready for its first trial. Wilbur won the toss of a coin and made the try. It was a cold day and the wind across the Kitty Hawk sands was only about five miles per hour. He did not get off the ground quite right. The Flyer came down about 100 feet from the starting point after being airborne only 2½ seconds. The machine suffered relatively minor damage, and it was agreed this performance didn't count as a real flight.

December 17, 1903, the Flyer was ready for another trial. Now it was Orville's turn. The wind was about 27 miles per hour. The machine started slowly along the 60 feet of launching track. After 40 feet, it lifted into the air, to fly 120 feet.

"This flight lasted only 12 seconds," Orville recorded the event ten years later, "but it was, nevertheless, the first in the history of the world in which a machine carrying a man had raised itself by its own power into the air in full flight, had sailed forward without reduction of speed, and had finally landed at a point as high as that from which it started."

There were three additional flights that bleak December day, with the brothers alternating at the controls. The longest and last, with Wilbur the pilot, was of 59 seconds' duration and was for a distance of 852 feet.

Earlier in the same month—December 8—the tandem monoplane of Samuel Pierpont Langley for a second time had become fouled on its catapult launching apparatus on top of a houseboat and had plummeted into the Potomac river. With that, Langley's dreams of a man-carrying airplane—buttressed by 17 years of effort and more than $70,000 of federal funds and money from The Smithsonian Institution—were shattered. Before that, other amply financed attempts, like those of Maxim and Ader, had come to grief. Engineers and scientists had applied themselves to the problem, only to fall short of the goal. Lilienthal and Pilcher had been killed by their aerial experimentations; the talented Pénaud, frustrated by obstacles, had committed suicide.

How was it, how could it be, that two young men from Ohio, without special training or special advantage, should succeed where all others had failed? Was it blind luck, some stroke of chance? Or could it be that the brothers from Dayton possessed a priceless kind of genius that made them different from all other men, a genius that reserved for them alone the prize of accomplishment?

The full story of Orville and Wilbur Wright—and what they accomplished—has been told many times. It may be possible, though, by focusing on some of its details, to provide essentials which will enable the reader to decide for himself just exactly what kind of miracle was wrought at Kitty Hawk.

Neither of the brothers was a graduate of high school, but this was due to lack of interest in diplomas rather than failure to absorb knowledge. Sons of a bishop of the United Brethren church, they early developed the habit of reading, to learn more about the many subjects in which they were interested. It was from such reading that they first became aware of the experiments of Lilienthal, and it was thus that they were infected with the aeronautical contagion.

Fully as important, they read critically. Even as they absorbed accounts of the faltering efforts by so many over the years to solve the problems of heavier-than-air flight, they pondered the "whys" of the unbroken succession of failures. They judged that Lilienthal had been correct in his approach (*see Chapter III*), but that he hadn't done enough.

"It seemed to us," Wilbur observed in 1901, "that the main reason why the problem had remained so long unsolved was that no one has been able to obtain any adequate practice. We figured that Lilienthal in about five years of time had spent about five hours of actual gliding through the air. The wonder was not that he had accomplished so little, but that he had accomplished so much. It would not be considered at all safe for a bicycle rider to attempt to ride through a crowded city street after only five hours' practice, spread out in bits of 10 seconds each over a period of five years; yet Lilienthal with his brief practice was remarkably successful in meeting the fluctuations and eddies of wind gusts. We thought that if some method could be found by which it would be possible to practice by the hour instead of by the second there would be the hope of advancing the solution of a very difficult problem."

When their own experience taught them how difficult it was to amass even a few minutes of gliding flight, they refused either to become discouraged or to attempt too rapid progress on the basis of shaky and incomplete information. On the other hand, the Wrights had divided the total problem into parts which could be attacked piecemeal, and they astutely made use of each nugget of information they gathered by experiment and thought. "The difficulties," to quote again from the Wilbur Wright of 1901, "which obstruct the pathway to success in flying machine construction are of three general classes: (1) Those which relate to the construction of the sustaining wings; (2) those which relate to the generation and application of the power required to drive the machine through the air; (3) those relating to the balancing and steering of the machine after it is actually in flight. Of these difficulties two are already to a certain extent solved. Men already know how to construct wings, or aeroplanes, which, when driven through the air at sufficient speed, will not only sustain the weight of the wings themselves, but also that of the engine and the engineer as well. Men also know how to build engines and screws (propellers) of sufficient lightness and power to drive the planes at sustaining speed. Inability to balance and steer still confronts students of the problem. . . . When this one feature has been worked out, the age of flying machines will have arrived, for all other difficulties are of minor importance."

In the spring of 1900 the Wrights were ready to move beyond

the first phase of study and speculation, which had lasted four years. In the second phase, they proposed to construct a glider and by its use to acquire the skill necessary to master the art of motorless flight.

This first of their machines was, in most respects, not markedly different from those used by earlier experimenters. It was of biplane design, much like the gliders Chanute had developed; except that it had a small horizontal control surface in front of the wings and it had no tail. Following the example of Lilienthal, the wing surfaces had a slight curvature from front to back.

In one vital particular, though, the original Wright glider was markedly different. Where others had sought to maintain equilibrium in flight by shifting the weight of their bodies, the Wrights devised a method of warping the wings to achieve lateral balance. Unlike the Chanute glider, their glider was not rigidly trussed from front to rear. By a cable arrangement linked to a cradle which the prone pilot moved with his hips, the wing tips could be twisted so as to present slightly varying angles to the wind, one up and one down.

Convinced of the rightness of their theory, they proceeded methodically to prove it. First they built a five-foot model, which they flew as a kite, with cords enabling the wings to be warped by an operator on the ground. Even when they had built their first man-carrying glider and had assembled it at Kitty Hawk, they flew it as a tethered kite until they had satisfied themselves of the correctness of the control device under full-scale conditions. Only then, by that time familiar with the characteristics of their machine, did the brothers make a dozen free flights from Kill Devil hill. Instead of expected hours of free flight, they had managed only two minutes!

In later years, it would be argued passionately that the Wright brothers were not the first to have had *the idea* of obtaining lateral control in flight by warping the wings. Notwithstanding, certainly, to them alone could the credit be given for reducing this idea to successful practice.

Although the performance of their 1900 glider had been gratifying with respect to attainment of satisfactory lateral control, the Wrights were puzzled by the fact that its lifting capabilities did not equal their expectations, which had been based on Lilienthal's tables of air pressure.

Chanute (*see Chapter III*) with whom they had become acquainted through correspondence, suggested that if they were to build a second machine, the wing curvature might profitably be made to correspond more closely to that used by Lilienthal. This advice they accepted, only to be greatly discouraged when they found in the summer of 1901 that the new glider, their second, had performance characteristics poorer than those of their original machine. Clearly, something was wrong. They rechecked their computations and decided that the errors most probably were in Lilienthal's tables of air pressures.

In 1908, writing for the *Century* magazine, they reviewed their processes and recalled: "We saw that the calculations upon which all flying machines had been based were unreliable, and that all were simply groping in the dark. Having set out with absolute faith in the existing scientific data, we were driven to doubt one thing after another, til finally, after two years of experiment, we cast all aside . . . Truth and error were everywhere so intimately mixed as to be indistinguishable."

Disillusioned, they undertook to make their own measurements and chose the wind tunnel as their research tool. It was a happy decision because their second tunnel, crude though it was by today's standards, provided the means of acquiring information which was gratifyingly accurate. Their first tunnel had been a makeshift device which they used only a short time. For months they worked, collecting and analyzing a fund of information which would later prove to be indispensable to them in designing their successful airplane.

They measured the aerodynamic forces on numerous airfoils and wings of different shapes and aspect ratio (length versus width), arranged in monoplane, biplane and triplane combinations. They quickly noted the aerodynamic superiority of the monoplane wing arrangement over the biplane positioning, but continued to favor the latter design practice for reasons of structural strength.

They decided their next machine would be more efficient if the wings had less camber or curvature but greater aspect ratio than previously used, and they found an airfoil which would provide adequate lift for an airplane with the amount of power they expected to obtain from an engine. They were following the lead of earlier experimenters in using curved (cambered) wings. But, by the skill of their own work they had also taken a giant step forward.

Perhaps most important of all, by this research they provided themselves with a set of tables upon which they could rely. Now there was justification to continue their efforts.

In 1902, the Wright brothers again went to Kitty Hawk with a new glider. Incorporating as it did the results of their wind tunnel work, they hoped it would perform more satisfactorily than had the others. They were not disappointed. So successful was the machine that they felt justified in returning to Dayton, there to begin design and construction of their first airplane and the motor to power it.

Theirs were not the first wind tunnels (*see Chapter II*). Nor was the wind tunnel the only way in which aerodynamic measurements could be made. But then and now, it was a device—once uniform air flow had been established, as they managed to do—which enabled them to obtain readily measurements of satisfactory accuracy. Dr. Langley had used a device with a whirling arm on which his airfoils were mounted, but here the measurements obtained might be in error because of the virtual impossibility of avoiding variations in wind velocity. At least equally difficult was the exacting task of obtaining reliable information from their experiments in the open, and never uniform, wind.

The Wrights were sound thinkers. They were tenacious in their search for information which could be accepted without reservation. They possessed the energy and the patience necessary to conduct the systematic investigations leading to solution of difficult problems. Too, the bachelor brothers were free from family responsibilities which might have lessened the intensity of their concentration.

The Wrights possessed a quality ascribed to men more often than is deserved—Yankee ingenuity. It was natural for them to make things which they lacked. As youngsters they had wanted a printing press larger than one available to them, so they constructed it themselves, using for essential elements the framework of a folding carriage top and parts fashioned from cord wood.

They became interested in bicycling, and this led to the opening of a sales shop, which inevitably was followed by development of a repair business. The final step was manufacture of their own line of 'cycles, of which several hundred were built and sold.

Of course, this kind of enterprise required a machine shop, and in it they built the parts for their gliders and then the 1903 powered machine. It was here, also, they operated their tiny aeronautical laboratory.

Here, too, was constructed the engine for the Wright Flyer, because the brothers had discovered, as did Langley, that no available engine combined required lightness with adequate power, and that no manufacturer would undertake to build one to their specifications. In construction of the engine, they were aided substantially by Charles E. Taylor, who was working for them in their bicycle business, but the design was theirs.

The design of the engine was straightforward enough; in fact, its four cylinders with bore and stroke of 4 inches conformed to automotive practice of their day. The crankcase and block were of cast aluminum, the cylinders and pistons of cast iron. Complete with accessories, the engine weighed only 170 pounds, developed 12 horsepower. It was a product characteristic of the Wright brothers; it was dependable if not fancy.

The problem of acquiring satisfactory propellers was fundamentally much more difficult. Orville and Wilbur looked to the shipbuilders for assistance and found that, after nearly a century, marine propellers were still being designed on a cut-and-try basis, and not too successfully at that.

So, starting with the then novel concept that the propeller behaved aerodynamically very much in the manner of a wing, they worked out a design which made every part of the propeller an airfoil. They achieved an efficiency of 66 per cent which was at once remarkable as well as essential to the success of their first flight attempts.

In their work, they showed themselves to possess the characteristics and talents of many professions and trades. They were craftsmen, knowledgeable in the fabrication of parts from wood and metal; in the best sense of the word, they were mechanics. They learned how to plan and conduct the systematic research which marks the scientist. They could break a complex problem down into soluble parts, and, conversely, they could visualize the individual pieces which could be fitted together into a workable whole; they merited the name of engineer.

They were remarkably self sufficient. Working together, thinking together, they conceived and designed and built and flew the world's first successful airplane . . . on December 17, 1903 . . . from the sands of Kitty Hawk.

# 6/ THE WRIGHT BROTHERS, AFTER KITTY HAWK

*The invention all admired and each how he,*
*To be the inventor missed; so easy it seemed,*
*Once found, which yet unfound*
*Most would have thought impossible.*
*Milton*

For Orville and Wilbur Wright, December 17, 1903, was bright with history-making achievement. It was, no less, a day when the glow of exhilaration fanned by their four flights was chilled momentarily by a blast of wintry wind. As if to teach the pioneers that their conquest of the air still was only a tentative thing, the wind picked up their Wright Flyer and rolled it along the sand.

However—as had been before and again would be—ribs and spars could be made anew. The brothers knew what they had accomplished; they hastened to send the telegram that told their kin in Dayton, Ohio.

The first newspaper accounts were friendly, albeit inaccurate in important detail. They attracted little notice in the United States. Perhaps the recent, widely publicized misfortunes of Professor Langley had convinced the American editors that the airplane was not to be taken too seriously.

Such was not the case in Europe. In the spring of 1903, interest in aeronautics on the continent had been stirred by Octave Chanute's detailed account of the gliding experiments of the Wright Brothers, presented at a meeting of the Aero Club in Paris. Now, cabled reports of the December 17 flights quickened the urgency with which experimenters, particularly in France, pressed forward. There were the scoffers—some would keep strong and vocal in their disbelief for years. More important, however, there were those who believed the accounts of the aerial miracle.

Before considering the struggles of others to fly, it may be fruitful to trace the further progress after December 17, 1903, of Orville and Wilbur Wright. A first step was to have the record set straight about their flights at Kitty Hawk. Late in December, Orville wrote to Ferdinand Ferber, an officer in the French army who had become interested in gliding experiments as early as 1898. Although he did not mention the distance of the fourth and longest flight, Orville stated its speed and duration, and Captain Ferber was able to calculate accurately how far the airplane had traveled. In January 1904, the Wrights issued a statement to the press, correcting inaccuracies in the first publicized accounts.

For some time both before and after December 17, 1903, the Wrights showed no great reluctance to talk of what they had done, and how. For example, Wilbur's statement in 1901 to the Western Society of Engineers, that as early as their 1900 gliding experiments, "the lateral equilibrium and the steering to right or left was to be obtained by a peculiar torsion of the main surfaces, which was equivalent to presenting one end of the wings at a greater angle than the other," and in the same paper, that "twisting the wings so as to present their ends to the wind at different angles is a more prompt and efficient way of maintaining lateral equilibrium than shifting the body of the operator."

In June 1903, Wilbur again spoke to the Western Society of Engineers. Now he told more about the successful use in flight of their wing warping technique: "when properly applied the means of control proved to possess a mastery over the forces tending to disturb the equilibrium. Since balancing was effected by adjustments of the surfaces, instead of by movements of weight, the controlling forces increased in power in the same ratio as the disturbing forces, when the machine was suddenly struck by a wind gust. For this reason we did not seem to experience the same difficulty in managing the machine in high winds, that Lilienthal who used a different system seems to have met."

Thus, the Wrights themselves had told, in general terms, how they achieved lateral stability. Chanute's Paris talk of 1903 included more specific information: "To assure transverse equilibrium, the operator works two cords, which warp the right and left wings and at the same time adjust the vertical rear rudder." That the Wrights came to regret such remarks is evident in their letter to the *Scientific American* in 1912, commenting upon the action of the German patent office nullifying the main claim of the Wright German patent application. This action, they wrote, was on the basis of prior disclosure contained in a European digest of the 1901 paper, and Chanute's Paris talk of 1903.

In May 1904, they were ready to begin flights with their new airplane. They invited the press to witness the trials, requesting only that sensationalism be avoided and that no pictures be taken. In all, some 50 persons, including a dozen newspapermen, were on hand at the Simms Station flying field, eight miles east of Dayton on the electric trolley line.

"When preparations had been completed," the brothers recalled in an article in the *Century* Magazine in 1908, "a wind of only three or four miles was blowing—insufficient for starting on so short a track—but since so many had come a long way to see the machine in action, an attempt was made. To add to the other difficulty, the engine refused to work properly. The machine, after running the length of the track, slid off the end without rising into the air at all. Several of the newspapermen returned the next day, but were again disappointed. The engine performed badly, and after a glide of only 60 feet, the machine came to the ground. Further trial was postponed 'til the motor could be put into better running condition. The reporters had now, no doubt, lost confidence in the machine. . . ."

During 1904, Orville and Wilbur Wright made 105 flights, many shorter than their best of December 17, 1903. Heavier and stronger than the 1903 Wright Flyer, their second airplane was in most respects similar to the original machine. It was powered by a new engine that produced some 17 horsepower, compared to the 12 hp. output of the 1903 engine. Speed was increased from 30 miles per hour to a full 34 mph.

Of the 1904 flights, Wilbur recalled in 1912 that "usually the machine responded promptly when we applied the control for restoring lateral balance (coming out of a turn) but on a few occasions the machine did not respond promptly, and the machine came to the ground in a somewhat tilted position. The cause of the difficulty proved to be very obscure, and the season closed without any solution of the puzzle."

But they had made significant progress in 1904. In September, they used for the first time their "derrick-catapult" which gave the airplane needed acceleration for takeoff. On September 20, they succeeded in making a full circle, and on November 7, a flight was made lasting a few seconds more than 5 minutes. Yes, the Wrights were surely learning how to fly!

For their 1905 flights they built a third machine, again using the 1904 engine, which by now had an output of 20 hp. As was the case of their second machine, the 1905 airplane was similar to the original Wright Flyer. They learned how to maintain good lateral control during turns by pointing the nose slightly downward. "In other words, the machine was in what has come to be known as a 'stalled' condition," Wilbur said in 1912, as he recalled the turning troubles that had taken them so long to overcome.

On December 15, 1905, Maj. B. F. S. Baden-Powell, president of the Aeronautical Society of Great Britain, was in the chair for the opening meeting of the 41st session of that body. It was then that Patrick Y. Alexander arose to present to the Society a letter written a month earlier by the Wright Brothers. It read in part: "during the month of September we gradually improved in our practice, and on the 26th made a flight of a little over 11 miles. On the 30th we increased this to 12⅕ miles, on October 3 to 15⅕ miles, on October 4 to 20¾ miles and on the 5th to 24¼ miles. All these flights were made at about 38 miles an hour . . . Unfortunately, we neglected to refill the reservoir just before starting (on the October 5 flight), and as a result the flight was limited to 38 minutes. We had intended to place the record above the hour, but the attention these flights were beginning to attract compelled us to suddenly discontinue our experiments in order to prevent the construction of the machine from becoming public. The machine passed through all of these flights without the slightest damage."

In 1903 the Wrights had flown; by 1905 they had learned how to fly—*expertly*. As Major Baden-Powell said with quite typical British understatement, "to remain half an hour in the air seems extraordinary."

Having convinced themselves that by now they had accomplished the task of developing a practical airplane, the Wright Brothers would not fly again until the spring of 1908. Next they undertook labors which proved equally difficult . . . they sought to sell their airplane, first to the United States and only after failure in their own country, to foreign powers. This period of negotiations, full of disappointments which would have frustrated less determined, single-purposed men than Orville and Wilbur Wright, one may pass over quickly, if regretfully.

But first, a portion from a letter the Wrights wrote Captain Ferber late in 1905. It was part of correspondence in which they had expressed willingness to sell their airplane to France. In a letter from Ferber, written immediately preceding the letter from the Wrights, he had told of progress he was making with a powered glider.

They wrote:

"France is indeed fortunate in finding a Ferber. We extend felicitations the more heartily because we do not believe that your success will decrease the value of our own discoveries. For when it becomes known that France is in possession of a practical flying machine other countries must at once avail themselves of our scientific discoveries and practical experience. With Russia and Austria-Hungary in their present troubled condition and the German Emperor in a truculent mood, a spark may produce an explosion at any minute. No government dare take the risk of waiting to develop practical flying machines independently. To be even one year behind other governments might result in losses compared with which the modest amount we shall ask for our invention would be insignificant.

"But even though France already has reached a high degree of success, it may wish to avail itself of our discoveries, partly to supplement its own work; or, perhaps, partly to accurately inform itself of the state of the art as it will exist in those countries which buy the secrets of our motor machine.

"Under the present circumstances we would consent to reduce our price to the French government to one million francs. . . ."

On May 22, 1906, the U.S. Patent Office recognized the specifications and claims of the Wright Brothers, filed March 23, 1903, by issuing Patent #821,393. Earlier in the year the Wrights had sent the Aero Club of America an account of their work. They noted their prime objective had been to "devise a machine of practical utility, rather than a useless and extravagant toy. For this reason," they continued, "extreme lightness of construction has always been resolutely rejected. On the other hand, every effort has been made to increase the scientific efficiency of the wings and screws (propellers) in order that even heavily-built machines may be carried with moderate expenditure of power." After observing that their engine possessed "no extraordinary qualities," the Wrights concluded with an aphorism that Benjamin Franklin would have been proud to claim, "the best dividends on the labor invested have invariably come from seeking more knowledge rather than more power."

In the autumn of 1906 in France, Santos-Dumont began public tests with an airplane. [More about the efforts of this wealthy Brazilian in Chapter VIII.] Reports in this country had Santos-Dumont flying for more than a kilometer on October 23. [Actually, he managed only 160 feet that day.] Orville and Wilbur Wright refused to become unduly concerned. They knew too well how long it had taken them, after December 17, 1903, to master fully the problems of stability and control, and to teach themselves the art of piloting.

So, in their quiet, unruffled way, they continued to seek purchasers for their invention. They reasoned, correctly, that in the European countries, which even then were engaged in the armament race that was to explode in the summer of 1914, purchasers sooner or later would be found, willing to do business on terms favorable to the Wright Brothers.

In 1907, Wilbur crossed the Atlantic to conduct negotiations with potential purchasers. Orville joined him later in the year. An airplane was shipped to France, but was to be left crated until the following year at the customs house in Le Havre.

Meanwhile, President Theodore Roosevelt had read an account of the Wright airplane in the *Scientific American* and had asked William Howard Taft, then the Secretary of War, to investigate. Such high level prodding brought the results which repeated efforts by the Wright Brothers themselves had failed to achieve. On December 23, 1907, the War Department issued detailed specifications for a military airplane. Bids were invited, with a closing date of February 1, 1908. The flying machine was to have a design speed of 40 mph in still air; for every mile below, a 10 percent penalty would be charged, and for each mile above, a 10 percent bonus would be paid. Required to convey two persons with "a combined weight of about 350 pounds" and also sufficient fuel for a flight of 125 miles, the airplane would also be required to make a nonstop flight of at least one hour.

The provisions of other specifications stipulated that "it is desirable that the flying machine should be designed so that it may be quickly and easily assembled, and taken apart and packed for transportation in Army wagons. It should be capable of being assembled and put in operating condition in about one hour . . . It should be so designed as to ascend in any country which may be encountered in field service. The starting device must be simple and transportable. It should also land in a field without requiring a specially prepared spot and without damaging its structure . . . The price quoted in proposals must be understood to include the instruction of two men in the handling and operation of this flying machine. No extra charge for this service will be allowed."

The situation existing in 1907–08 was recalled in 1913 in London by Lt. Col. George O. Squier, USA, who had been in charge of the acceptance trials, and was later to become Chief Signal Officer. He said, "you must remember that the Government had recently granted £10,000 to Professor Langley for experimental work. At that time his accomplishments were not generally appreciated, and the support accorded him was regarded by many as a waste of public money. It will be apparent, therefore, that the public was in no mood at the time to listen favorably to any proposal to spend still more money on aircraft. But, the Wright Brothers came to the War Department and informed us what they could do, and they so convinced the authorities that money was found to give them their first contract . . . The issue of the contract was criticized severely, and the War Department was supposed to have lost its head.

"Coming from the Government, the contract helped the Wrights in France and elsewhere . . . It is hardly believable, but five years ago the first specification for airplanes ever contracted for was drawn up in the American War Department in one afternoon, and on a single sheet of paper."

In March 1908, the Wrights sold their French rights for about $100,000 plus half the founders' shares in the French company which was to be formed. The contract was conditioned upon two demonstration flights of about 31 miles apiece, each to be accomplished within an hour. The demonstrations had to be completed by the end of October.

With the practicality, the unwillingness to leave anything to chance, which characterized Orville and Wilbur Wright in everything they did, the brothers now went again to Kitty Hawk to sharpen the piloting skills which had lain idle since October of 1905. They used their 1905 machine, which had been modified to carry a passenger for the first time. Both pilot and passenger sat upright in this version, and the controls, previously operated from the prone position, were changed accordingly.

Late in May, Wilbur again sailed for France. It was not until August 8 that he made his first flight from foreign soil, using the Hunaudières race course at Le Mans, some 125 miles from Paris, as his flying field. French pilots had by now made many flights, covering distances of 12 miles or more. The many delays which held up Wilbur's first French flight served only to strengthen the popular belief that the American was a huge "*bluffeur*."

But now, in two short flights, Wilbur Wright dispelled all doubts. What the French had seen from their own countrymen had been like the ponderous cavortings of so many aerial Dumbos, compared to the grace of a darting swallow. The French press went wild; the somber-faced Wilbur was their darling.

On September 3, 1908, Orville made his first flight at Fort Myer, across the Potomac from Washington. On September 9, he made two record flights, the first 57 minutes long, the second, one hour, two minutes, 15 seconds in duration. Almost daily he flew for a longer period. Official Washington was in a state of happy amazement.

Then came September 17. Days earlier the then Maj. George O. Squier, in charge of the acceptance trials, had flown as a passenger. So had Lieut. Frank P. Lahm. Lieut. Benjamin D. Foulois, who weighed only 130 pounds, was well liked by Orville, who would have been pleased to have him as the observer-passenger on the official trial. But, instead, it was Lieut. Thomas E. Selfridge who made the flight that day. (Selfridge's earlier work with the Aerial Experiment Association will be told in Chapter IX.) As they flew at an altitude of about 75 feet, one of the propellers struck and ripped off a stay wire of the rear rudder. The airplane went out of control and smashed to earth. Selfridge was fatally hurt; he never regained consciousness. Orville was severely injured, suffering broken ribs and a fractured thigh.

Four days later, as if to show the world what stuff the Wright Brothers were made of, Wilbur flew nonstop for one hour, 31 minutes, 25 seconds. After this he continued to make long flights, sometimes with a passenger. By his seeming abandon and his demonstrations of perfect control he amazed and delighted all Europe.

On the last day of the year, Wilbur Wright flew 77 miles nonstop in two hours, 20 minutes, winning the Michelin prize of 20,000 francs for his exploit.

Acclaimed by all at the end of 1908, Wilbur and Orville Wright had reached the zenith of their career. They had blazed the trail; they had shown the way. Ahead for the two brothers who worked as one lay other honors. Ahead, no less, lay tragedy; 1908 had been their golden year.

# 7 / BRITISH AND OTHER AIRPLANE BUILDERS

*Certainly many birds of good wing would bear up a good weight as they fly; and spreading feathers thin and close, and in great breadth, will likewise bear up a great weight, being even laid, without tilting at the sides. The farther extension of this experiment might be thought upon.*

*Francis Bacon*

European efforts to learn the secrets of heavier-than-air flight, at the beginning of the 20th Century, were sporadic. The deaths of such gifted experimenters as Lilienthal and Pilcher, the frustrations of such men of means as Ader and Maxim had occurred close to home.

In Europe, however, the urge to fly was nonetheless strong; military minds foresaw advantages to be gained from panoramic aerial reconnaissance conducted at great height. For some years most men would seek another path, the lighter-than-air way. To them, the carrying capabilities of a hydrogen-filled dirigible offered a rational solution to the weight problem presented by the bulky, low-powered engines of the day.

There were, however, more than a few who lived for the day when they could harness power to fragile craft made of wood and fabric, and so equipped, take to the air. [In France alone, the number of aeronautical experimenters to be recalled in the period between 1900 and 1909, is so large as to require all of Chapter VIII.]

Such a person was Wilhelm Kress, an Austrian engineer and piano manufacturer, whose dreams of flying had been made the more intense from watching Lilienthal gliding in 1896. The earlier models which Kress made were based upon bird shapes, but the full-scale airplane he built largely of light steel tubing had three wings in tandem; it was equipped with a rear rudder and elevator. By October 1901, he was ready for flight trials from the surface of Tullnerbach lake. Kress was the first to use a gasoline engine to power a man-carrying airplane. But the manufacturer had far exceeded the engine's anticipated weight, and the craft, mounted on two floats made of aluminum, refused to become airborne and overturned when it hit a rock.

In Europe, as in the United States, there were those whose efforts to perfect an airplane were carried on under such conditions of privacy as to make difficult attempts to determine, in later years, who had been first in accomplishment. In Denmark, J. C. H. Ellehammer, an engineer, began construction of a monoplane as early as 1904. Powered by an engine rated at 18 hp., his airplane was tethered to a pole for its first tests.

Later, in the work he conducted on the island of Lindholm, Ellehammer converted his airplane to a biplane. He used a tractor propeller, and wheels for his landing gear. On September 12, 1906, he reportedly made a flight or hop of 138 feet, rising about six feet above the earth. [It was not until October 23, 1906, that Alberto Santos-Dumont flew 160 feet in France; the pioneering of the Brazilian is told in the next chapter.] In 1908, at Kiel, Ellehammer made the first flight from German soil. In addition to his work with monoplane and biplane, he also constructed a triplane. His accomplishments, reported or real, were soon surpassed by those who followed. Nonetheless, the Dane was an aeronautical trail blazer.

What many of the European experimenters of the period were seeking was inherent, or automatic, stability for their aircraft. Where Orville and Wilbur Wright attempted to learn how to achieve lateral control through the pilot's precise manipulation of wing-warping—and succeeded brilliantly—many of the Europeans wished for built-in stability that would provide maximum safety in flight. Efforts were made in various ways to obtain inherent stability; to a remarkable extent some workers attained this goal. In speed and maneuverability, however, their airplanes proved themselves inferior; in later years it would become apparent that pilots preferred more agile performers whose stability, at least in part, depended upon the skill of the man at the controls.

Another European worker in the period immediately following Lilienthal was José Weiss. A Frenchman working in England, Weiss was an engineer and a painter. He, too, sought to achieve inherent stability using natural forms. His work, begun about 1896, led to construction of some 200 models during the period 1902–07. Most of the Weiss models were birdlike in appearance; in fact, for his experiments he was in the habit of using dead birds, their bodies and wings stiffened for the work at hand.

Beginning in about 1906, there worked with Weiss a young electrical engineer, Frederick Handley Page. In March 1909, Handley Page, who at the time was forming his own manufacturing company, exhibited at the first British aero show a monoplane, based upon the work of Weiss, which was as yet unflown. The price tag was £500, but as a journal of the day observed, "the flyer is naturally somewhat rough-and-ready in appearance, for practically the whole of the framework is built up of cane . . . which does not lend itself very well to neat jointing."

The record shows that the bird-shaped design was "not outstandingly successful." The ideas of José Weiss could not long compete with those of the more vigorous, more practical aeronautical workers who followed. However, as will be told in Chapter XV, Handley Page went on to design and produce aircraft that would make his name world known in aeronautics.

Among those who studied stability as shown in natural phenomena was a German professor, Friedrich Ahlborn of Berlin. He became especially interested in the broad-winged seeds of a tropical vine *Zanonia macroparpa.* As the seed carrier of this vine ripens and dries, the leaflets wither and curl. Weighted at the front by the seed itself, the result is a stable gliding mechanism which carries the seed for considerable distances.

Ahlborn's studies became known to a number of aeronautical experimenters, among them the Austrian engineer, Igo Etrich. Another who had been inspired by the work of Lilienthal, he did his basic experimentation in the years between 1899 and 1906. Etrich was assisted in his efforts by Franz Wels; first he designed and built gliders, and then a birdlike monoplane. By the end of 1909, his plane had been flown from the aviation ground at Wiener-Neustadt for distances of 2¾ miles or more, and at speeds up to 40 mph. A measure of inherent stability was attained by means of swept-back wings and upturned wing tips. Where the influence of Weiss on the shape of later airplanes was slight, Etrich's monoplane, called the *Taube* (German for dove) became the progenitor of a class of German aircraft widely used in the early years of World War I. The Taube type, in later years, appeared in both monoplane and biplane form.

Another to give careful attention to the structure of the *Zanonia* seed carrier as suggested by Ahlborn was J. W. Dunne. A Briton, he had begun his aeronautical work as early as 1900, when he experimented with rotary wing aircraft designs. In about 1904, he turned his attention to the possibility of attaining an inherently stable aircraft, and during the next two years he made a great number of small paper models to test the validity of his ideas. On the basis of this work, which resulted in a tailless design with the main planes swept back to form a "V," Dunne was employed by the British War Office in 1906 to design and build a powered, man-carrying airplane. His machine was tested as a glider in 1907 under conditions of secrecy. The following year, with a 20 hp. engine, Dunne's aircraft reportedly rose from level ground under its own power.

Directional control of the Dunne airplane was obtained by the operation of flaps or ailerons. Worked together they gave longitudinal control; worked independently or in opposite directions, they provided lateral control. Where Dunne came by his ideas for obtaining directional control is not clear. It might have been that he became familiar with the manner in which the Wright brothers obtained lateral control; as was detailed in the previous chapter, the Wrights, and Chanute, by 1903 had made public essential details of the wing warping technique.

In 1909, Dunne left his government work and by the next year had completed a large biplane which was flown in public with considerable success. On December 11, 1910, he made a demonstration flight before two men acting as observers for the Aeronautical Society of Great Britain, Griffith Brewer and Orville Wright.

Their official report follows:

"Yesterday afternoon we observed two flights by Mr. Dunne on his automatic stability machine, at the Royal Aero Club ground at Eastchurch.

"The first flight was over a distance of about three miles (not timed), the machine being turned at a height of about 100 ft. and making a good landing near the starting point. On the second flight of 2 mins. 29 secs., Mr. Dunne made notes on a piece of paper during the flight. On both flights the engine was cut off before landing and the machine came down without materially altering its angle of incidence."

/s/ Orville Wright, Griffith Brewer
Members of the Aeronautical Society

"The paper (see above) was not stiff and necessitated the use of both hands in order to write these pencil notes, thus showing that both hands were off the levers for sufficient time to make these notes during the actual flight. In descending, after having cut off the engine, Mr. Dunne held both arms up in the air and resumed hold of the handles just prior to making the actual landing."

/s/ Griffith Brewer

The stability of the Dunne machine was gratifying; in 1913, the Burgess Company of Marblehead, Mass., secured American patent rights and built a number of aircraft, both landplanes and seaplanes, from the original Dunne design. Several Burgess-Dunne airplanes were bought for the U.S. Army Signal Corps and the Navy.

Still another European who sought to design and build an inherently stable airplane was Anthony H. G. Fokker, "the flying Dutchman." His story might well come somewhat later, because his first airplane did not make its first flight until the end of 1910; it is told here principally because it reflects a view not uncommon at the time, which was that there must be another way of obtaining lateral stability than that used by the Wrights.

In Fokker's words, as set forth in his autobiography, "I made hundreds of wood and paper models with the idea of analyzing their movements in an effort to solve the problem of lateral stability. I hung pendulums from the center of some of these models, but I found the pendulum merely imparted a systematic swinging motion to the airplane, putting it into a series of banks. By endlessly trying wings in every conceivable kind of position, I finally came to the conclusion that a sweepback wing with a pronounced dihedral, combined with a high center of gravity, would give me an airplane of perfect lateral stability.

"When I actually had found an airplane which was inherently stable, I decided that it was not necessary to warp the wings as the Wrights and others had done before Glenn Curtiss invented the ailerons. For that reason my first monoplane was built two years later (1910) along my own lines, without ailerons. It has a high center of gravity and V-shaped sweepback wings, and practically perfect stability."

In later years, to gain greater maneuverability, Fokker abandoned the features which provided his airplanes with automatic stability, and after brief use of wing warping, he adopted ailerons.

In Germany, especially, emphasis on lighter-than-air ships slowed development of the airplane. Zeppelin's first rigid airship made successful flights beginning in July 1900; not long thereafter, funds to continue his work were forthcoming from the Imperial Government. Beginning about 1906, the ideas of von Parseval and of von Gross for semi-rigid airships received strong support from the Kaiser.

One of the few German aeronautical workers to concentrate upon heavier-than-air ideas was Hans Grade who, despite lack of encouragement both practical and moral, succeeded in making flights up to a thousand feet, or more, by the end of 1908. His first work had been with a triplane design, but his first brief flights were in a monoplane. In 1909, Grade won a $10,000 prize for being the first in an all-German airplane to make a figure "8" in flight.

The Grade monoplane—it was flown nonstop for as long as 54 minutes in 1909—had a fuselage of steel tubing and tricycle landing gear, fitted with pneumatic tires. The wings were braced at top and bottom by wires, and wing warping was used. The pilot sat below the wings in a hammock seat suspended by springs from the framework tubing. The airplane was powered by a 20 hp., 4-cylinder, air-cooled engine which Grade had also built. A metal two-bladed tractor propeller, attached directly to the crankshaft, was used.

In a journal of the day, the similarity between the Grade machine and the tiny "Demoiselle" [described in a later chapter] which Santos-Dumont was flying in France was noted. Another writer saw in the Grade airplane a blend of the Bleriot and Santos-Dumont machines, with a tail of the Antoinette type! He went on to observe that the sweep of the wings was suggestive of the Taube design. It is to be doubted the similarities were entirely coincidental; after all, for a very long time, imitation has been the sincerest form of flattery.

In Italy, too, despite the fact that lighter-than-air experiments attracted most interest and effort, there were those who felt that the airplane held great promise. Enrico Forlanini, an Italian engineer, constructed an airplane model as early as 1885; it was rocket-powered and was accelerated along two steel wires prior to free flight. About 1904, Forlanini—who later became well known for his work with airships—built a boat which ran along the water on small vanes or hydroplanes. He conceived his boat as a step intermediate to an airplane which would take off from water.

Among other early Italian airplane experimenters were Arturo Crocco and Gianni Caproni. Best known in his early years for work with airships, and in his later life for the leadership he gave to aeronautical research in Italy, Crocco as early as 1903–04 had designed an airplane in which automatic longitudinal stability was to be provided by "an elastic articulation through which the wings assumed the necessary incidence," and lateral stability was to be controlled by the pilot who manipulated a lever thus to move "the two wings oppositely." Stability considerations aside, the model built by Crocco is even today strikingly modern in appearance. It was a cantilever monoplane, well streamlined. It had a cruciform tail and power from the submerged engine was shafted to the propeller in the tail.

Caproni began to dream of airplanes, and to ponder the problems requiring solution, even before he completed his training as a civil engineer in 1907. The following year he studied electrical engineering, but the aeronautical fever began to burn hot within him. Despite financial difficulties, he decided his career lay in the sky, and by 1910 he was soloing in his own airplane.

Despite the fact that Igor Sikorsky did not build and fly his own airplane until 1910, and despite the fact that his earliest work was directed towards development of a helicopter—work that was performed 30 years too soon—the name of Sikorsky cannot be omitted from any listing of early European airplane pioneers. As a child in Russia he learned from his mother about Leonardo da Vinci's attempts to design a flying machine; as early as 1901, when he was 12, Sikorsky was making helicopter models. In following years, his models grew in size up to ones that had a pair of rotors 30 inches in diameter.

It was not until 1908, however, when he left the family home at Kiev for a summer in Germany, that Sikorsky began to concentrate upon aeronautics. In 1909, he went to Paris and talked with men who had actually flown. More important, he bought a 25 hp. Anzani air-cooled engine, taking it back to Russia for future use.

There, Stefan Drzewiecki strongly advised him to stop wasting his time on helicopters. A countryman of Sikorsky, Drzewiecki was a Polish-born engineer-scientist whose work with propeller theory was an independent development in detail of the propeller theories of the famous English marine engineer, William Froude. Though Sikorsky was impressed by the source of the advice, he was not easily discouraged and by the spring of 1910 had built two unsuccessful helicopters. By now convinced that solution of problems peculiar to the helicopter was a still distant goal, he turned to construction of airplanes. Within a matter of weeks he had built two. In the first, he hopped, but unsatisfactorily. In the second, in the summer of 1910, he made his first real flights. By the end of the year he was fairly launched upon a career in aviation that would make him world known as a pioneering builder of aircraft.

Finally, for this chapter, consider two other pioneers who did their best to develop airplanes in Great Britain at a time when the Royal Navy was still thought to be the only protection that would ever be needed. The first of this pair was Alliott Verdon Roe who, after years as an apprentice in the factory of a locomotive manufacturer, had enjoyed some success as a motorcycle racer. He had then become a marine engineer; after several years at sea, he settled down in England to work for industry.

By 1906, young Roe had become convinced the reports that Orville and Wilbur Wright had flown distances up to 20 miles were true. Once convinced, he forthwith penned a letter to *The Times* of London, expressing his firm belief in the reports, and adding that, provided he could build a full-size airplane similar to models he had already made and tested, he too could fly. *The Times* commented that it, most certainly, could not "in any way adopt the writer's estimate of his undertaking." The letter went on to say that "all attempts at artificial aviation on the basis he describes, are not only dangerous to human life, but fore-doomed to failure from an engineering standpoint."

But to the London *Daily Mail* "engineering standpoint" was no deterrent to circulation-building model airplane contests, and in 1907 Roe proceeded to win the cash prize from some 200 other entrants. That same year he built a full-size biplane; in June of 1908 it was ready for testing. Fitted with a 24 hp. Antoinette engine, Roe's airplane succeeded in rising from the ground for short distances. But, a committee of the Royal Aero Club decided in 1929, these experiments could not be considered free flight.

Financial stress forced Roe to part with his French engine. To power his second airplane, a triplane completed in 1909, he had to resort to an engine with considerably less horsepower. In June of that year, he wrote that: "I have been making dozens of short flights with my British-built airplane during the last few weeks; true, they are hardly more than jumps, being only 2 or 3 feet high and 50 or so feet in length. . . . To be candid, to carry 40 lbs. per hp. has proved a bigger task than I calculated on, for my machine, with self aboard, weighs 400 lbs., and is driven by a 10 hp. J.A.P. motorcycle engine . . ." But, once started, Roe went forward with great speed; he is another of the men whose names will appear again, as builders of aircraft which enjoyed success in the years leading to World War I.

It was probably inevitable that S. F. Cody should have been

called Colonel—even Edward VII is said to have addressed him so. Although he was American-born and had indeed been both cowboy and goateed performer with a Wild West show, he was not the original "Buffalo Bill" Cody. By 1905, he had graduated from traveling with a circus troupe and was attracting public attention with man-lifting kites he had built. That year one of his kites lifted a man to a height of 2,600 feet, and Cody went to work at the Balloon Factory of the British Army. Soon he was engaged in airplane construction, as well as in designing and building a dirigible. No engineer, Cody was a good mechanic; he had the patience to build and rebuild until he was satisfied with what he had done.

The first of Cody's airplanes was a biplane; it combined Wright glider characteristics with those of his kites. It was powered by an Antoinette engine. In 1908, he reported to the Aeronautical Society, his airplane had left the ground:—"I made a machine that left the ground the first time out; not high, possibly five or six inches only. I might have gone higher if I wished. I made some five flights in all, and the last flight came to grief . . ." On the next to last flight, according to Cody, he flew 200 feet; on the last, he swerved to avoid trees and crashed.

Rebuilt and modified, Cody's airplane was again flown in 1909. In May he flew for more than a mile. That summer he installed an 80 hp. E.N.V. engine and in September made a cross-country flight of 40 miles. Cody's best known airplane was his "Cathedral," which he built in 1910, having severed his connections with the War Office because that British agency felt $12,500 was too much money to spend on the efforts of Cody and Dunne, working independently. The wing span of his "Cathedral" was 43 feet, and Cody mounted ailerons between the wings as Curtiss had done. Cody, by now a British subject, went on to win some $50,000 in prizes before being killed in an airplane accident in 1913.

Yes, in Europe during the years after 1900, from Land's End in England to the banks of the Dnieper in the Russian Ukraine, there were not a few who labored long and diligently to design and build and fly heavier-than-air machines. Some of these Europeans were consciously seeking to follow the ideas of Lilienthal; some of the experimenters were obviously inspired by the successes of the Wright

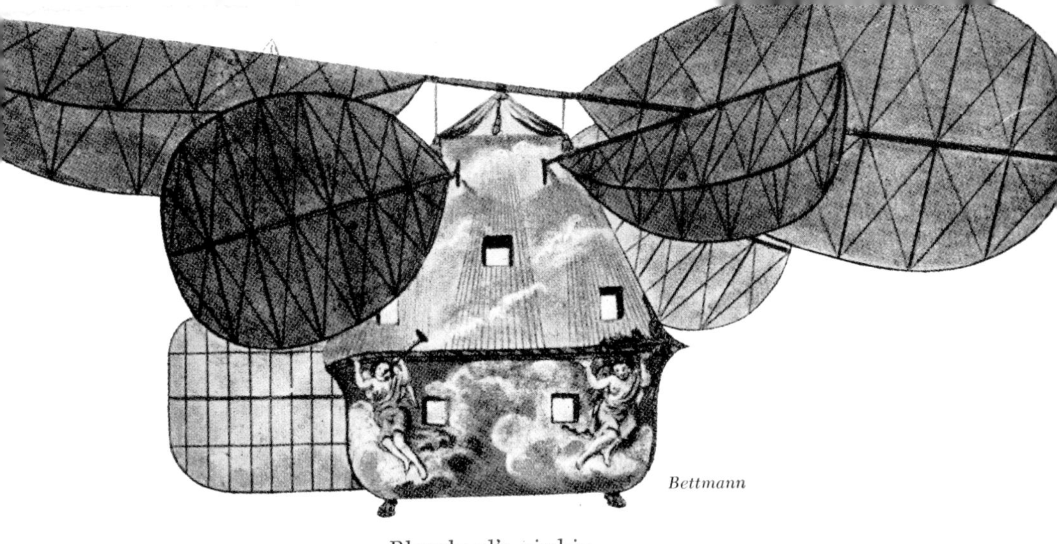
Bettmann

Blanchard's airship.

Heinmuller

Garnerin's parachute.

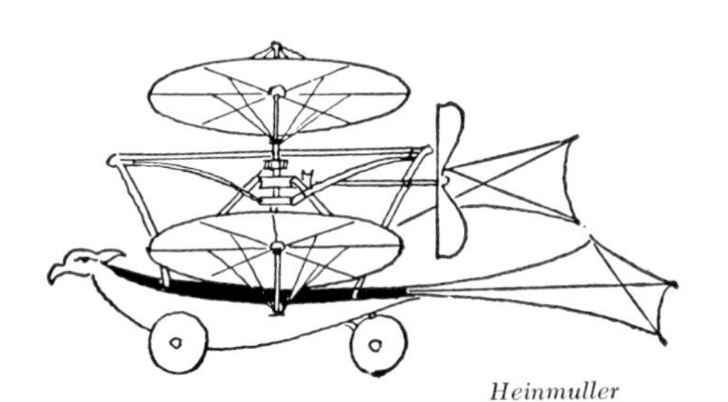
Heinmuller

Cayley's aerial carriage.

Bettmann

De Groot's flying machine.

*Bettm*

Friar de Gusmão's "passarola."

A French writer foresaw in 1781, the "paratrooper" of some future air war.

*Bettmann*

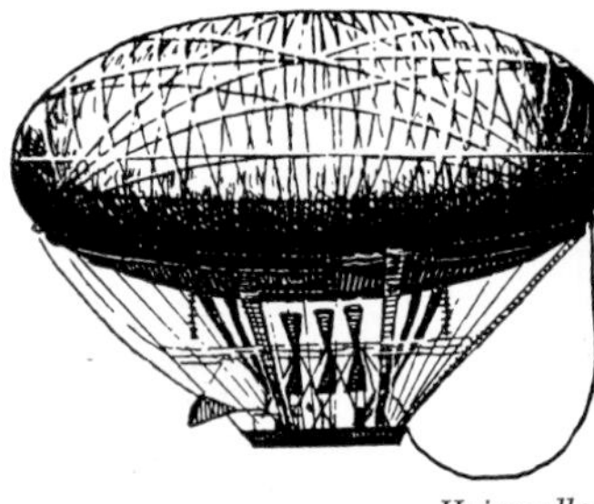

*Heinmuller*

Meusnier's ellipsoidal airship

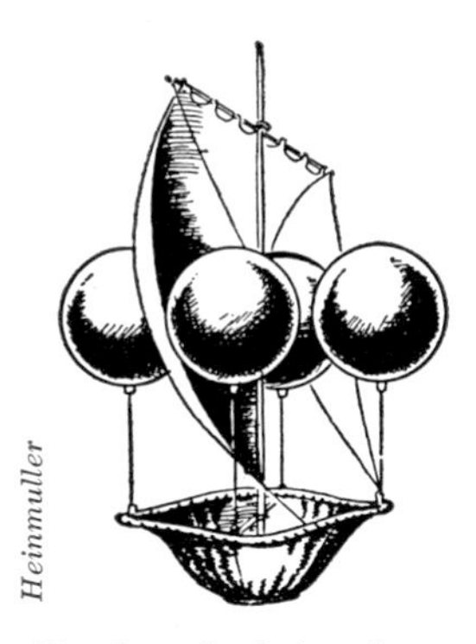

Heinmuller

De Lana's flying boat.

Bettmann

A special Pegasus with lyre attached for poets.

Guncotton was to supply the rocket thrust for this "jet job" design created in 1847.

Bettmann

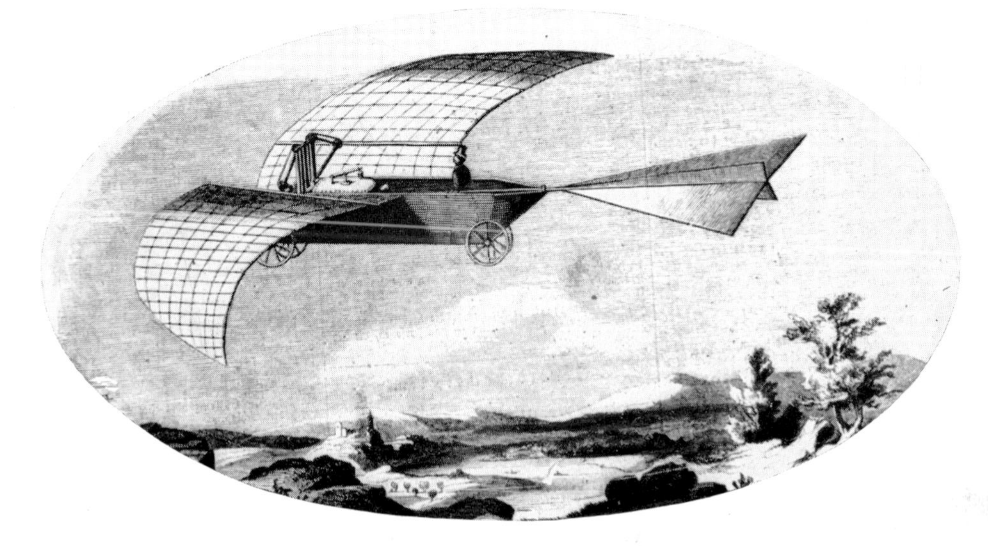

Heinmuller

Maxim's flying machine.

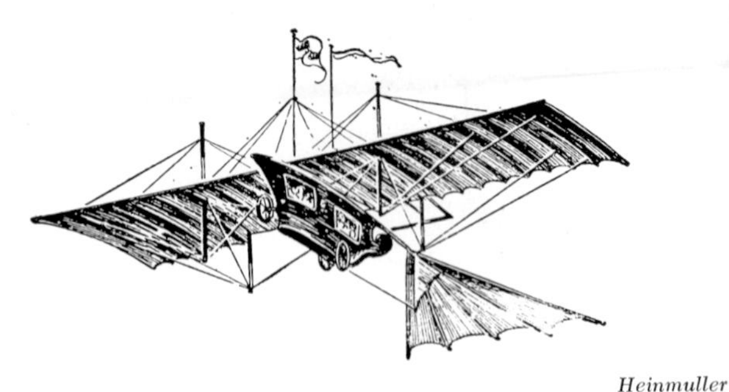

Heinmuller

Henson's aerial steam carriage.

This "White Cruiser of the Clouds" anticipated, as far back as 1882, the eventual arrival of the helicopter.

Bettmann

Heinmuller

Launoy and Bienvenu's early helicopter design.

Bettmann

Intrepid aeronauts soar through the air at Ze lendorf, near Berlin, an 1899 version of t glider developed by B tenstedt.

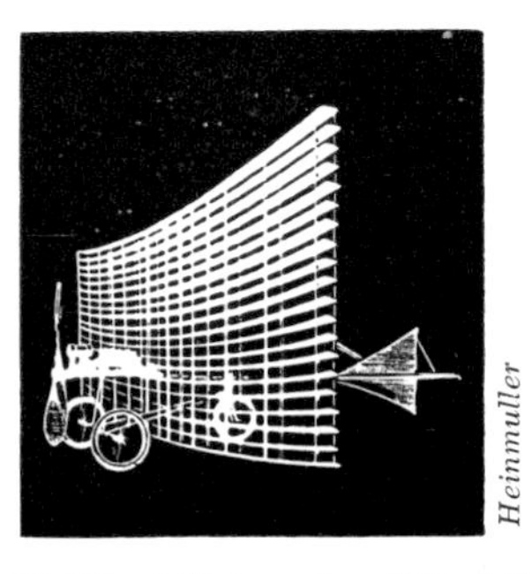

Heinmuller

Phillips' "Venetian Blind."

Compressed air, in the two drums, was slated to propel Ayre's machine (1885).

Bettmann

Bettmann

Badgley, in 1879, foresaw aerial navigation.

*Scientific Gentleman* termed Lewis' 1876 flying machine "a decided wonder."

Bettmann

*Bettmann*

Pilcher's glider.

*Bettmann*

Chanute's glider.

Kress' seaplane.

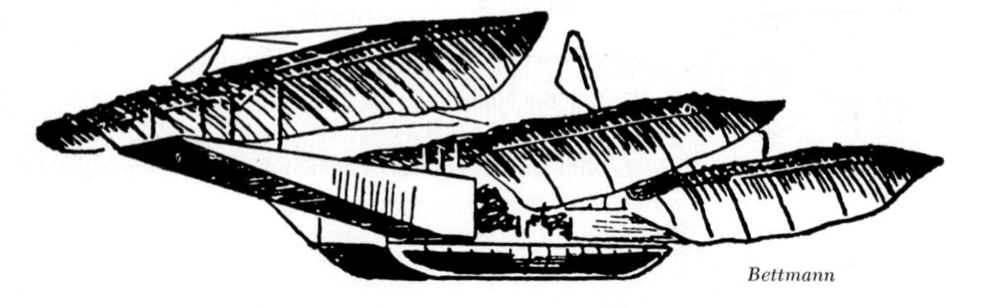

*Bettmann*

*Bettmann*

An artificial hill near Berlin was the site of Lilienthal's first glider experiments, in 1891.

*Heinmuller*

Ferber glider.

*Heinmuller*

The Flying Tricycle.

Percy Pilcher is shown soaring in his "Hawk" glider, weighing about 50 pounds.

*Library of Congress*

Bettmann

Glider built and flown by Octave Chanute.

Bet

A ground view of Chanute's glider.

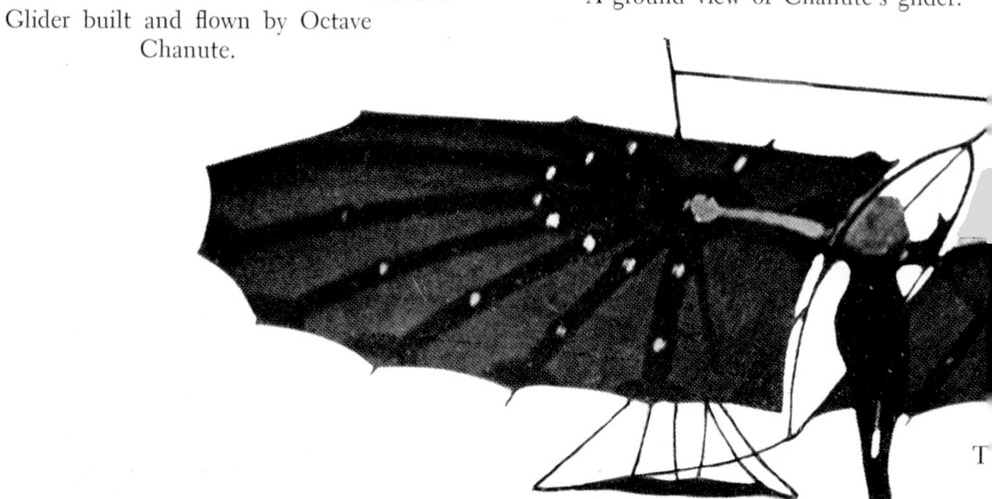

T

Wilbur Wright—Kitty Hawk—1902: the threshold of powered flight.

*Smithsonian Institution*

This 1890 model was powered by rubber bands in tension and a geared propeller.

*Smithsonian Institution*

Langley's devoted assistant, Charles M. Manly, was at controls of the aerodrome.

*Smithsonian Institution*

ken in 1894 in Germany, ienthal in his glider.

*Smithsonian Institution*

In 1887, Langley devised a catapult to get his small models into the air.

*Library of Congress*

This drawing by Arnold Boecklin, a painter, of the airplane he built (1881–1885), shows an attempt to increase wing area.

*Bettmann*

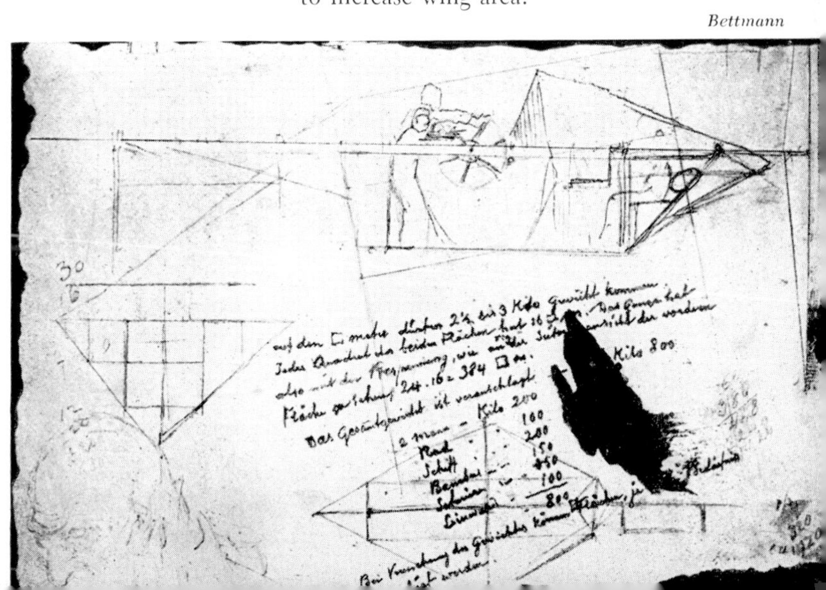

Smithsonian Institution

This engine produced 54.4 horse-power, and could reach a maximum of 850 rpm.

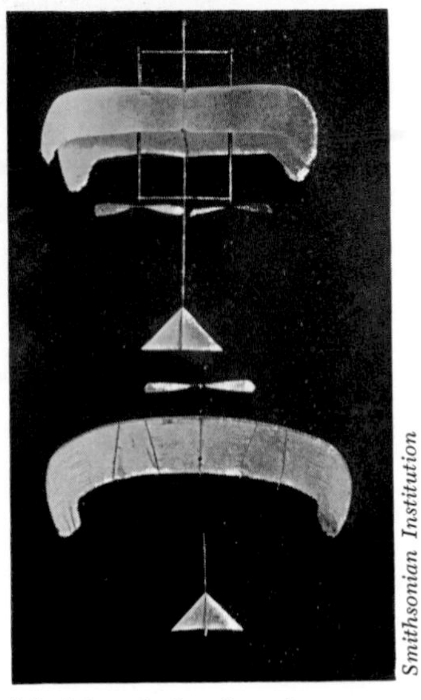

Smithsonian Institution

Models of the Langley tractor monoplane, pusher bi-plane.

Langley's Aerodrome No. 5 flew under its own power, without pilot, on May 6, 1896.

Smithsonian Institution

This quarter-size Langley model, used for testing balance and rigging, was flown in August, 1903.

Smithsonian Institution

*Smithsonian Institution*

On October 7, 1903, Langley's aerodrome was poised on its launching catapult.

*Smithsonian Institution*

A mechanic cut the cable . . . "there was a roaring, grinding noise."

*Smithsonian Institution*

Then rowboats sped to pick Manly, unhurt, from the Potomac River.

COLLAPSE OF THE AIRSHIP.

# AIRSHIP FAILS TO FLY

## Prof. Langley's Machine Goes to River Bottom.

## PROF. MANLY ABOARD

### THE LATTER RESCUED FROM PERILOUS POSITION.

Test of th[...] Off the Arsenal [...]

had proved successful it would have had a free flight up three branches of the stream.

**Construction of the Airship.**

The airship itself is built of slender steel tubing and wooden supports. It has four sixty-foot wings, two propellers and a rudder propeller. The wings and their supports are not attached to the machine until just before the time for the flight, and the propellers and other detachable parts are not assembled until after the machine has been placed on the launching car. To handle the heavy wings and canvass propellers in a strong wind is out of the question, according to the opinion of the experts in charge of the tests, and the prospect of a test Saturday was dissipated by a strong wind which began in the morning and gradually increased in velocity.

Sunday no work was done on the houseboat, but Monday the workmen were on hand early and started in to prepare for a test. Ice covered the river, except in the main channel, an[...]ather was cold and biting. Pr[...] a trip [...]wn [...]mac [...]

*Washington Evening Star*

Finally, in 1914, at Hammondsport, N.Y., the Langley aerodrome—modified and fitted with floats—was flown; the flight fanned the flames of the controversy.

*Smithsonian Institution*

This is the flight the world commemorates—a powered plane first carried man Dec. 17, 1903.

*Smithsonian Institution*

*Henry Ford Museum*

The original shop in which Orville and Wilbur Wright made parts for their Kitty Hawk airplane has been transplanted from its Dayton site to the Henry Ford Museum.

*Smithsonian Institution*

Orville Wright.

Wilbur Wright.

It was in this crude wind tunnel that the Wright Brothers tested out their theory of aerodynamics.

*Smithsonian Institution*

In 1903, the Wrights built the engine that was to make possible at last their dream of powered flight.

*Smithsonian Institution*

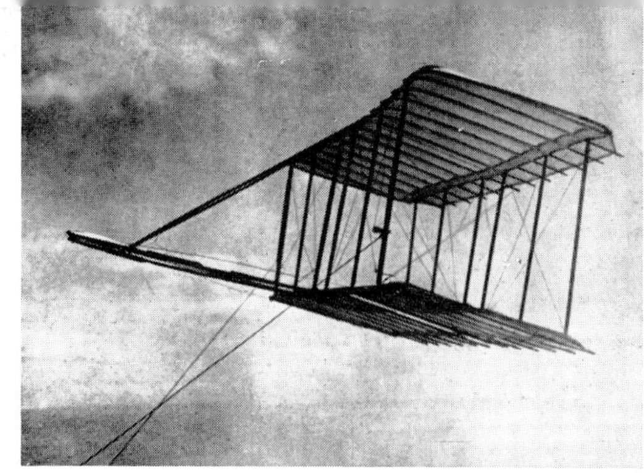

*Smithsonian Institution*

These three photos depict how the Wrights' gliders developed in the era just before Kitty Hawk.

*Smithsonian Institution*

*Smithsonian Institution*

On a flight the Wrights discounted, Wilbur flew 2½ seconds and covered 100 feet on December 14.

*Smithsonian Institution*

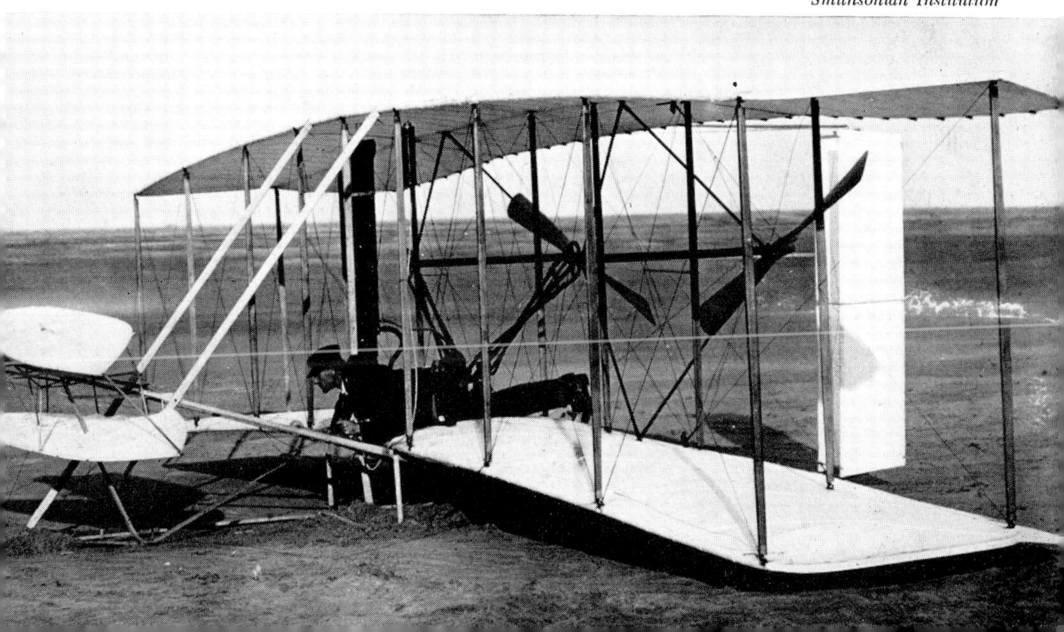

*Library of Congress*

In 1904 the Wright Brothers began using a catapult device to improve the launches of their "flyer."

The Wright military plane of 1908 met the test of being transportable by wagon.

*Smithsonian Institution*

brothers. Some of the airplanes were patently imitative of the craft constructed by others. Some of the attempts to fly were clumsy and faltering. And yet progress, real progress, was being made. In Europe, during the first decade of the 20th Century, men were taking to the air—in their own airplanes.

# 8/ THE FRENCH PIONEERS

*The star is not extinguished when it sets*
*Upon the dull horizon; it but goes*
*To shine in other skies, then reappear*
*In ours, as fresh as when it first arose.*
*Horatius Bonar*

The brothers Montgolfier in 1783 had constructed the hot air balloon which enabled J. F. Pilâtre de Rozier to become history's first man to fly. With this paramount aeronautical achievement their inheritance, it was not strange that—once they were aroused after the turn of the 20th Century—the proud French should make strenuous, if not immediately fruitful, efforts to assert leadership in development of the airplane.

Earlier, the 19th Century work of Pénaud and Ader was described (*see Chapter II*). Mention also might have been made of Victor Tatin who, as early as 1879, constructed a monoplane model powered by a compressed air engine, which made several tethered flights. In later years, Tatin resumed an active interest in aeronautical experiment, as will be noted.

At the beginning of the 20th Century, French aeronautics was, to be kind, in a state of confusion. After the modest, but real, successes—by the Tissandier brothers in 1882, and by Renard and Krebs in 1884—had demonstrated the possibility of building powered, navigable airships, French development of lighter-than-air craft had faltered. At the close of the 19th Century, Alberto Santos-Dumont, and the well-to-do sugar refiners, Paul and Pierre Lebaudy, among others, revived French interest in airships, but by then the Germans across the Rhine had taken a commanding lead in lighter-than-air developments.

At the beginning of 1900, so far as heavier-than-air experiments in France were concerned, Ferdinand Ferber was probably the most active and articulate. An artillery officer with technical training, he was teaching at the military school at Fontainebleau in 1898 when, like the Wright brothers, he became inspired by reading of the gliding experiments of Lilienthal. The next year, Ferber built his first glider, a canvas covered affair with some 80 square feet of supporting surface.

By the time he had built his fifth glider, in 1902, Ferber was in lively correspondence with Octave Chanute, and the biplane construction he used reflected awareness of and admiration for the early gliding successes of the Wrights. Early in 1903 he cried with Gallic intensity, the airplane must not be allowed to be perfected first in America, but when the first reports were published about the December 17, 1903 achievements of the Wrights, Ferber was among the relatively few in Europe who accepted the accounts as literally true.

Ferber is credited with inspiring men such as Ernest Archdeacon and Gabriel Voisin, about whom more later, to vigorous aeronautical effort. At the same time he was lecturing and writing, Ferber continued his own experimentation. In about 1904, he fitted a 6 hp. Buchet engine to his Wright-type glider, and tested it at Nice, with unspectacular results. It was tethered to a merry-go-round device.

Ferber became acquainted with Léon Levasseur, the French builder of powerful, lightweight engines used in motorboats. Government money was not available to buy such a powerplant, and so it was that the "Antoinette" engine was first used to power other airplanes. Ferber flew in 1908, but the brief success he enjoyed as a pilot was due largely to flights he made in Voisin biplanes.

"To design a flying machine is nothing; to build one is nothing much; to try it in the air is everything." This thought, which he expressed not long before his death in 1909 following a crash landing, had been Ferber's rule and guide for a decade of experimentation. Despite the energetic and forthright manner in which he had sought to develop his own airplane, Ferber's influence on French aeronautics—and it was not insignificant—was more than anything the result of his bestirring of others to activity.

In his own modest estimate, Ferber had acted as a ferment and a popularizer. But he was proud that he had belonged to the great school of experimenters, Lilienthal, Pilcher, Chanute, and the Wrights—and he felt he had helped to put France on the right aeronautical course.

Another to have great influence upon the burgeoning French effort to design and build and fly airplanes was, himself, no Frenchman. It was in Australia that Lawrence Hargrave did his work in aeronautics. His experiments were carried on for a period of nearly 25 years, beginning in 1884. Hargrave, who declined to patent his innovations, regularly reported the progress he was making, usually in papers read before the Royal Society of New South Wales. Chanute not only was familiar with Hargrave's work but helped to make them more widely known through his own writings.

For several years, Hargrave experimented with flying models. In this period his interest was primarily ornithopters. He made some 50 models with flapping wings. For power he used clockworks, rubber in tension, compressed air, and steam. Flights up to several hundred feet in length were made. He also experimented with propeller-driven models.

It was Hargrave's work with cellular kites, begun about 1893, that proved to be of greatest interest to the French. In his experiments Hargrave was soon flying box kites, somewhat similar to those patented in 1871 by Danjard. His kites resembled large honey-comb structures fastened to the opposite ends of a stick parallel to the axis of the cell membranes. Hargrave learned that if he made his kites with curved surfaces, convex side up, they developed almost twice the lift of those with flat surfaces.

In 1896, Hargrave made public his conclusion that in the construction of an airplane, use of box-kite construction would afford the stability and lift of a monoplane wing with pronounced dihedral and of twice the span. Airplanes which Santos-Dumont and the Voisins, among others, built in France were characterized by the cellular construction of Hargrave's box kites.

The son of a wealthy coffee planter from São Paulo in Brazil,

Alberto Santos-Dumont was still in his teens when he arrived in Paris in 1891. First automobiles and then navigable balloons were objects of his fast-running enthusiasm. One must pass quickly over the story of how, between 1896 and 1905—when he turned his attention to heavier-than-air craft—Santos-Dumont pressed steadily forward his development of dirigible balloons. Suffice it to say, his exploits during this period captured both the fancy of the French populace and, in 1901, the 125,000 franc prize offered by a patron of French aeronautical experimentation, Henri Deutsche de la Meurthe, for a 7-mile flight circling the Eiffel tower.

Throughout his career, Santos-Dumont repeatedly faced disaster, and yet he was never seriously injured. In 1905 he began experimenting with a glider, patterned after the Hargrave cellular kite, which was towed by one of his airships. In that year, too, he built his first airplane. He called it his "No. 13 *bis*" or #13½, extending the lineage of his airships. The success that this effort enjoyed, if it can be called success, was so limited that Santos-Dumont often referred to the "No. 14 *bis*" as Biplane #1.

Santos-Dumont experimented with his "No. 14 *bis*" during the summer of 1906 at Bagatelle, and flew or hopped for a few feet on August 23. On September 14, he made another try, with a number of witnesses present. He was aloft for 8 seconds but the distance traversed was not measured. On October 23, Santos-Dumont flew again; this time he had notified the Aero Club of France he wished to try for the 3,000 franc prize offered by Ernest Archdeacon for the first flight in Europe of more than 25 meters (Ellehammer's earlier attempts in Denmark were not known at the time in France). His attempt was a success; he traveled 164 feet, nearly twice the required distance. Finally, for 1906, he made three flights on November 12. The distance covered by the third was 721 feet.

Santos-Dumont's airplane was essentially two three-cell kites, forming the main wings. They were attached to the fuselage in which he stood erect. The wings had a marked dihedral to assure a measure of stability. The only means for control was by a third single-cell box kite which was positioned at the forward end of the fuselage and which could be moved up and down. (Additional lateral control was later sought by use of movable planes or "curtains" in the outer cells of his wings.) A two-bladed propeller was attached by direct drive to the Antoinette engine. The first of the Levasseur-built engines Santos-Dumont used developed 24 hp.; the second was rated at 50 hp.

Looking for all the world as if it were flying backward, Santos-Dumont's "14 *bis*" was constructed of steel tubing and bamboo, with fabric covering for the wings, fuselage, and control surfaces. The wings had a span of about 40 feet, with a supporting area of 860 sq. ft. Total weight, including the flyweight Santos-Dumont's 110 lbs. and the larger engine, was only 645 lbs. Wing loading was figured at ½ lb. per sq. ft., compared to about 1½ lbs. per sq. ft. for the Wright Flyer. The power loading was 13 lb. compared to about 42 lb. for the Wright airplane. At first the landing gear had four wheels; later only two wheels were used.

With its "tail first" arrangement, and lacking effective control, Santos-Dumont's biplane craft exerted little lasting influence, except for its use of cellular kite construction, upon the design of other airplanes which soon were built in France. But, by his public performances in 1906, faltering though they may have been, he dispelled all doubt in Europe that man could fly.

In France and elsewhere, the continued reticence of the Wright brothers to fly "in the open" until negotiations for sale of their invention proved successful, had increased skepticism about whether they had actually flown. Perhaps typical was Captain Ferber. In 1903 he had accepted reports of their Kitty Hawk flights at face value; later he openly doubted their achievements.

The following year Santos-Dumont had another airplane constructed, similar in most respects to his 1906 machine. In it he made several flights, as long as 656 feet and 476 feet; in 1907 he was unable to better his own flight of 721 feet of the previous year.

The airplane for which Santos-Dumont is perhaps best known was his tiny monoplane which weighed only 259 pounds. The fuselage of the "Demoiselle"—dragonfly—was a triangular frame. It was 17 feet long and made of bamboo poles. The pilot sat below the 18-foot span of the fragile wings with their 102 sq. ft. of supporting surface. The engine was a 2-cylinder, water-cooled Darracq, developing 25 hp., which drove a 2-bladed wooden tractor propeller.

The whole tail moved on a universal joint. Wing warping was used, and three bicycle wheels served as the landing gear.

In September, 1908, Santos-Dumont flew the "Demoiselle" non-stop for eight minutes—after a takeoff run of only 65 feet. The following year he flew cross country, 4¾ miles in 5 minutes. The Dragonfly was difficult to fly, but the fact that it weighed less and cost less than a 1909 motorcycle made it popular. For a number of years it was built in modest numbers by Duthiel and Chalmers, and by the Clément-Bayard Company.

Santos-Dumont took out no patents on his airplane designs. Perhaps his most prized possession was a gold medal presented by the Brazilian government. On one side were the words, *"Por ceos nunca d'antes navegados."*—"Through skies never before navigated." For him it was enough that his airplanes had made flight history.

One comes now to a point in the account of airplane development in France where one must introduce Gabriel Voisin and his brother, Charles. Their aeronautical endeavors were so multi-sided and so energetic as to make it difficult, if not impossible, to discuss numerous other experimenters in France—among them, Archdeacon, Delagrange, Farman, Bleriot—without first considering the contributions of Voisin Frères to the work of each of these pioneers.

Ernest Archdeacon, a Parisian lawyer who was active in the affairs of the Aero Club of France, was one of the first to be stirred to activity by the 1903 exhortations of Captain Ferber that something must be done quickly if France hoped to be first in development of the airplane. With M. Deutsche de la Meurthe, Archdeacon gave of his wealth to the art and science of aeronautics in France.

But Archdeacon went further. In 1903 he had a glider, "du type de Wright," constructed for him at Chalais-Meudon. There is little indication that much was done with this, Archdeacon's first machine, until early in 1904, when Gabriel Voisin joined enthusiastically in the work. Soon, both men were making gliding hops among the sand dunes at Berck-sur-Mer, but this location was far from ideal, and they returned to Paris. Next, attempts were made to become airborne in the glider as it was towed by automobile across the drill ground at Issy-les-Moulineaux. The dangers of such experimentation were emphasized when the glider, being flown as an unmanned kite, was smashed in an accident in March, 1905.

Now, Archdeacon and Voisin together designed, and Voisin built, a second glider. It was equipped with floats and differed considerably in appearance from the craft of the Wright brothers. Perhaps for the first time in European aviation, the cellular structure of the Hargrave box kite was employed. The biplane wings were divided into three cells by four vertical "curtains." The forward elevator recalled Wright practice. No provisions were made for lateral control, but added was a large two-celled tail.

In June, 1905, while towed by a motorboat on the River Seine, at Billancourt, Voisin lifted the glider to a height of 50 feet or more, and remained airborne for a distance of perhaps 500 feet. Not long after, the close association between the two men was dissolved, and thereafter, Archdeacon was content to play the part of a strong supporter of aeronautics.

At about the same time, in fact, that the glider was being built for Archdeacon, Voisin undertook construction of a similar machine for Louis Bleriot, a well-to-do manufacturer of automobile headlights who, since 1900 had become increasingly engrossed by the determination to build and fly an airplane. The Bleriot glider was not unlike Archdeacon's except that the tail was a large, single cell, and also, that the lower of the biplane wings was shortened so that the outer "curtains" came downwards and inwards. Tested on the Seine, in the same manner as had been the Archdeacon glider, Bleriot's machine made a sudden dive into the water. Voisin nearly lost his life before he could extricate himself from the submerged wreckage.

In 1905–06, Gabriel Voisin went into partnership with Bleriot. During this period, two more Bleriot machines were built. The first was a sort of tandem biplane, the wings of which were large elliptical cells. A rudder was centered between the rear wings, and two 25 hp. Antoinette engines drove a pair of tractor propellers. The second was similar except that the forward biplane wings were quadrangular cells. The tests of this pair of aircraft, conducted from Lake Enghien near Paris, and at Issy-les-Moulineaux, were uniform failures.

Before the end of 1906 the Bleriot-Voisin partnership had been dissolved (details of Bleriot's subsequent work will soon be told) and Gabriel Voisin established himself as a custom builder of aircraft. It is clear that in this new venture, Voisin operated in a manner calculated to please his clients. However much he may have preferred to build aircraft along design lines which his considerable —for the times—experience had led him to believe were sound, Voisin knew that men willing and able to pay for construction of aircraft wanted them built to their own specifications.

It is to be suspected, however, that Gabriel Voisin was something of an idea salesman in his dealings with clients. Most of the airplanes he built in this period were basically similar.

In his work as an airplane manufacturer Gabriel Voisin was joined by his brother Charles, who also became a pilot. Voisin Frères soon employed the services of an engineer, Maurice Colliex. They made use of a wind tunnel. The Voisin brothers provided a real and valuable service to aeronautics; they were in fact the first commerical manufacturers of airplanes.

First among the "custom airplanes" which the Voisin factory turned out in 1907 was one to the order of Henry Kapferer, who became better known as an aeronaut, the pilot of the Surcouf dirigible, *Ville de Paris*. This airplane quickly disappeared from public view.

Next, the Voisins built airplanes for two young sportsmen, Leon Delagrange and Henri Farman. The former had enjoyed a fair measure of recognition as a sculptor; now he wished to make a name for himself as an aviator. The latter was English born but he had lived so long on the Continent he considered himself French. He had been a painter, a champion cyclist and an automobile racer.

Details of the 50 hp. Antoinette-powered Voisin biplane pusher design will be presented later by way of comparison with those of the Wright Flyer. Here it is enough to say that the Delagrange and Farman biplanes which the Voisin brothers constructed were generally alike except in minor detail. For example, on both airplanes, the landing gear was fitted with pneumatic tires, but the wheels of the Farman machine were mounted on casters which permitted them to swivel as they ran along the ground, while the wheels of the Delagrange vehicle were mounted without casters. Also, the Farman biplane made use of "curtains" stretching vertically between the wings to provide lateral stability, while the Delagrange airplane did not.

In March and April, 1907, with Charles Voisin the pilot, the Delagrange biplane flew at Bagatelle for short distances, and in November, Delagrange himself was making flights. Farman's airplane was completed in September and by the following month its owner was making flights longer than a thousand feet.

Beginning in 1908, Delagrange and Farman engaged in a public demonstration of aerial rivalry at the military drill ground at Issy-les-Moulineaux which the Minister of War had made available to the Aero Club of France. On January 13, Farman won the 50,000 franc Grand Prix d'Aviation Deutsch-Archdeacon for the first circular flight of 1 kilometer. He covered 1.6 km., about a mile.

In March, flying around a course marked by poles 500 meters apart, Farman flew about a mile and a quarter, while the best Delagrange could do was just short of a mile. The same month Delagrange's airplane also became the first in Europe to carry two men, Farman and Delagrange. By the end of April, when the aviators separated, Farman going to Belgium and Delagrange to Italy, the latter had increased the official record around the 500-meter course to about 6 miles.

By now Delagrange also had added "curtains" to his airplane. For about a year, Delagrange continued to use the Voisin biplane, in Belgium, Denmark and England, as well as in France. Then he began flying monoplanes built by Bleriot. In January, 1910, using a 50 hp. Gnome rotary instead of the 25 hp. Anzani for which his airplane had been designed, Delagrange crashed at Bordeaux, and was killed. Earlier, he reached a speed of 49.9 mph. in this airplane.

Henri Farman, too, was best known in 1908–09 as a pilot. In his Voisin-built biplane he made flights of 24.5 and 25 miles at Chalons on September 29 and October 2, 1908. Four weeks after the second of these exploits, Farman made the first cross-country flight, 17 miles between Bouy and Rheims.

Before entering the world of aviation, Henri Farman, in addition to his racing experience, had been involved in the manufacture of cycles and automobiles with his brothers, Maurice and Richard. In 1909, he designed and constructed his own biplane. It reflected the Voisin influence, but important modifications had been made. Both the fuselage and forward elevator were lighter, and a 50 hp. Gnome rotary engine was installed. The "curtains" were no longer in evidence, and flaps or *ailerons*—about which more later—were used.

The same year, 1909, Maurice Farman built his own modification of the basic Voisin design. The airplanes which the Farman brothers designed and built—they soon shared manufacturing facilities—were slow and cumbersome. And, at least by comparison with the designs which others soon produced, they were ugly.

"*Voila, les vaches mechaniques!*" . . . mechanical cows . . . was the way a French general reacted, and the epithet stuck, with some Maurice Farman aircraft being called "Longhorns," others, "Shorthorns." But they were safe to operate, and for several years to come, were widely used for training and other purposes.

Before considering the work of others it may be in order to return for a moment to the Voisin brothers and their planes. They built for many of the early fliers. In 1908, for example, J. T. C. Moore Brabazon—later Lord Brabazon of Tara—learned to fly in a Voisin. He then bought one of the Voisin planes (its name was "Bird of Passage"), and took it to England.

The Voisin influence, transmitted through the Farman aircraft, was large in the British-built Bristol "box kite" of about 1910. In World War I, Voisin aircraft were still being used. The imprint of the Voisin Frères upon the course of aviation was greater and more lasting than is generally known, at least in the United States.

To attempt to chronicle the aeronautical experimentation by all who worked in France during the early years of the 20th Century, would require far more space than is presently available. So, excepting three men whose activities require fuller treatment, one must be content with little more than mention of a few of the very considerable number of the other French pioneers.

Men, for example, such as Trajan Vuia, a Hungarian engineer living in France, who constructed a monoplane in which he made short hops in 1906 and 1907. It was powered by a carbonic acid motor of about 25 hp., which had a duration of only 3 minutes. In 1908 he also built a folding-wing, roadable airplane but it enjoyed little success.

In 1907 Alfred de Pischoff made several flights in a small biplane, including a 1-km. flight in December of that year. In 1908 he was flying a tandem monoplane of his own design. The Comte Henri de la Vaulx was credited with a flight or hop of 60 yards in November, 1907. Ernest Zens was flying in 1908 in a biplane powered by an Antoinette 50 hp. engine.

Although there is no evidence that his work had much influence on those who followed, Mons. P. Roux deserves mention for his experimentation with an "*oiseau mechanique*"—mechanical bird. It had flapping wings and was tested in 1904 by launching from a track like a roller coaster.

Louis Breguet was active in aeronautics during this period, but his earliest work, the preface to almost a half-century of leadership in aviation, was with a cumbersome, vertical-lift vehicle. It was called a gyroplane and was best known for its performance in 1908 when it inched its way upward to a height of 14 feet and traversed a distance of 60 feet. By 1909, Breguet had turned his attention to fixed-wing aircraft. The biplanes he began to build soon became well liked, and sales orders resulted.

Nor should Victor Tatin go unmentioned for his 20th Century work. He is credited with having collaborated on the designs of both the airships and the airplanes which Santos-Dumont built and flew. There is evidence that Bleriot's first successful monoplane was influenced by Tatin, and in 1909 the Clément Bayard organization—perhaps best known for its manufacture of airships—thought well enough of his ideas to build a Tatin-designed pusher biplane. Still later, about 1910, Tatin and Louis Paulhan, known principally as a pilot, built a monoplane which was driven by power shafted from the forward-mounted engine to a propeller behind the tail.

One comes now to Léon Levasseur, whose progressive work, both with engines and airplanes, made him a leader during the early years of powered flight. In 1903 he built a large monoplane which was unsuccessful. It was, however, notable because it was powered by an engine of his design, the predecessor of the Antoinette.

Levasseur was an engineer associated with Jules Gastambide, the financier. It was Gastambide's daughter's name that was chosen for both the lightweight engines, and, later, the airplanes which Levasseur designed; in fact, the company formed to construct the engines and the aircraft was also named Antoinette.

Beginning in 1905, production of the Antoinette engine was begun, for use in motor boats. Early versions of the engine provided 24 hp., approximately twice that available to the Wright brothers in 1903. The 24 h.p. Antoinette weighed only 120 lbs. compared to 179 lbs., for the Wright engine. Soon, Levasseur was building a 50 hp. Antoinette producing 1 horsepower per 5 pounds of weight. As indicated earlier, it was the Antoinette engine which Santos-Dumont, Bleriot, and the customers of the Voisin brothers used to power their airplanes.

As Albert Zahm wrote in 1911, "with an Antoinette in hand, what live man, particularly what live Frenchman, could tinker long years on the sand hills? Why not mount the craft on little wheels and take a cautious little run; then after some adjustment, make more runs followed by innocuous saltatory flights?"

In a later chapter devoted to power plants, the 50 hp. Antoinette engine which was Levasseur's most successful effort will be described in detail. Here it is enough to observe that it was a V-8, and that it employed fuel injection instead of carburetion. Cooling water turned to steam in the cylinder jackets, condensed in aluminum or copper tubes along the forward fuselage, and then was pumped back to the jackets.

Levasseur's airplane was a monoplane, one of the most graceful craft built prior to World War I. It first appeared in 1908, after production of a less successful monoplane, the Gastambide-Mengin, the year before. After experimentation and modification, the Antoinette monoplane was essentially standardized in 1909. Considered advanced in design, its wings were double surfaced and the fuselage was also fabric covered. In addition, both wing surfaces and fuselage were lacquered to reduce drag. The tail unit had both rudder and elevator. The landing gear was light in construction and included both a skid and pneumatic-tire wheels.

The Antoinette airplane was perhaps best known for the flights made in 1909, by Hubert Latham. That year he established endurance records for monoplanes and on June 7 carried the first monoplane passengers. The whole world was watching, July 19, when he took off from the French Coast on the first attempt to cross the English Channel in an airplane. Some 7 miles out he was forced down by engine trouble. Rescued by a French torpedo boat, Latham made a second try on July 29. This time he was within a mile of the British Coast before recurrence of engine trouble again forced a water landing. In 1910, Latham came to the United States with his Antoinette. In October, Baltimore was thrilled by his daring flights over the city.

In 1910 other, more dependable engines had been developed, and other airplanes, more popular by virtue of the exploits of their pilots, hurt sales of the Antoinette. Nonetheless, during the brief hour he was privileged to lead in French aeronautical development, Levasseur gave a mighty impetus to the efforts of many to fly.

Another Frenchman whose work prior to 1910 reflected advanced aeronautical practice was Robert Esnault-Pelterie. He was among those who became interested early in the work of the Wright brothers with gliders and in 1904–05 he carried on his own gliding experiments. The glider he built, with one exception, followed scrupulously the Wright design. The exception was Esnault-Pelterie's use of "horizontal rudders" at the end of each wing, instead of wing warping. In this work, he had his glider towed by an automobile. The lack of communication between the pilot and the driver proved to be a near fatal flaw in the arrangement and Esnault-Pelterie almost lost his life in a crash.

He was a leader in the French school which saw design advantages of the monoplane outweighing those of the biplane. Esnault-Pelterie is credited with having demonstrated that the drag produced by a thin wire—such as was used in bracing biplane wings—was far greater than its dimensions might seem to indicate.

By October, 1907, Esnault-Pelterie was flying in his own R.E.P. monoplane powered by his own R.E.P. engine. Its wings were braced internally, and the main landing gear consisted of two wheels, one large and one small, in tandem on the longitudinal centerline of the covered fuselage. Light wheels attached to the wing tips were employed while taxiing.

The second monoplane Esnault-Pelterie built, in 1909, was an improved version of its predecessor. The fuselage was made of welded steel tubing, and was fabric covered. The fabric-covered wings were quite thick for the times, and were made up of wooden ribs with the spars being constructed of steel, aluminum, and wood. The wings were faired into the fuselage. The 30 hp. engine was air-cooled and the five cylinders were arranged like an open fan. All in all, the design of the second R.E.P. monoplane was most advanced.

Perhaps, Esnault-Pelterie was too far ahead with his innovations to influence the progress of aeronautics as greatly and as immediately as did others who sought less radical ways by which to develop a practical airplane. Certainly, his ideas about streamlining and use of internal bracing to reduce drag, to say nothing of the construction methods he employed or of his work to develop an improved, simple control system, would be adopted in later years. For his own part, Esnault-Pelterie continued to think far ahead. In 1931, for example, he announced design of a rocket he hoped could make possible a journey to the moon with travel time 49 hours each way. Finally, for this chapter, one returns to consideration of Louis Bleriot. As early as 1900, he had become interested in aeronautics, and that year he endeavored, without success, to build a flapping-wing flying machine. After 1904, he abandoned work on ornithopters and began to experiment with gliders and powered machines incorporating the concept of the Hargrave boxkite.

Before the close of 1906, Bleriot's association with the Voisin brothers ended, and soon he was fairly launched upon what would be his greatest achievement, development of a successful monoplane. In 1907 he built three aircraft. The first of these he called the *Canard*—duck. It was a monoplane with paper covered wings, and its fuselage was partially covered also. There was a monoplane elevator in front; the 24 hp. Antoinette engine powered a pusher propeller at the rear adjacent to the vertical rudder. In April it made short hops, but the same month it was smashed beyond repair.

Next, Bleriot built a tandem monoplane which he christened *Libellule*—dragonfly. Outwardly it resembled the Langley "aerodrome." The wings had a surface of 194 sq. ft. and were covered by tough parchment paper. The outer sections of the forward wings could be pivoted independently. Later, Bleriot abandoned this device for lateral control in favor of the Wright's wing warping. In this machine he used first a 25 hp. and later a 50 hp. Antoinette engine. In the "Libellule," Bleriot flew a number of times during the summer of 1907. His best distance was 200 yards on September 17; the same day, his monoplane was completely wrecked.

In his third 1907 airplane Bleriot made use of the planform of the modern monoplane. There was the fuselage with engine and tractor propeller in front of the wings. Elevators and rudder were at the rear. A two-wheeled landing gear had a shock-absorbing mechanism. For control, Bleriot abandoned the "winglets" and instead, rigged the elevators so they could be operated separately for balance, and for climb or descent.

Bleriot also developed and standardized Alphonse Pénaud's concept of the control column—and patented his improvement. Bleriot's forerunner of the "joystick" rocked about a universal joint, with wing warping (or aileron) and elevator wires attached to a *cloche*—a bell shaped fixture—at the bottom of the control stick. Rudder movements were made by the feet on a bar.

Beginning in September, 1907, Bleriot practiced extensively with his new monoplane. By December, he was making turns in the air, and he managed flights of about ⅓ mile and speeds approaching 50 mph. In February, 1908, as he attempted to turn at low level, the inner wing tip dug into the ground, and another of Bleriot's aircraft was smashed.

But, as always, Bleriot began at once to build a new airplane, in which he flew 8½ minutes in July, 1908. That year he displayed two other craft, a monoplane and a biplane, at the Aero Salon in Paris. In October he flew his newest monoplane on a cross-country journey of 17½ miles. November 4, seeking to duplicate his cross-country exploit in foggy weather, Bleriot smashed into a tree. Again his craft was demolished; again he escaped serious injury.

Now, Bleriot began construction of his #11, the monoplane that would bring him lasting fame and fortune. It was not greatly different from its immediate predecessors except that it was smaller. Wing span was 25½ feet, and fuselage length 25 feet. First, Bleriot installed a 30 hp. R.E.P. engine; later he used a 28 hp. 3-cylinder, air-cooled Anzani. The laminated Walnut tractor (built by Chauvière, who was becoming quite popular as a propeller-building specialist) had a 6.6-ft. diameter and turned at 1,400 rpm. Weight without pilot was only 462 lbs.

The fuselage was rectangular and made of four ash members supported at intervals by vertical struts, the whole being trussed by diagonal wires. The wing framework consisted of two wooden spars, crossed by curved ribs. The fuselage was covered about half way to the tail. The wings were double surfaced, and the wing tips were rounded.

First flight of the #11 was on January 23, 1909, but it was not until July 25 that Bleriot made history in his new plane. At 4 a.m. that day, still limping from a leg injury suffered in an earlier accident, Bleriot climbed aboard his craft at Sangatte on the French Coast. Once aloft, he circled the field twice and then, at 4.35 a.m., headed across the Channel toward England. The weather was hazy; a French torpedo boat was standing by.

In a translation of Bleriot's own account of the flight:—"Below me is the sea, the surface disturbed by the breeze, which is now freshening. The motion of the waves beneath me is not pleasant. Within 10 minutes I have passed the torpedo boat, and I turn my head to see whether I am proceeding in the right direction, but I see nothing—neither the torpedo boat, nor France, nor England; I am alone. For 10 minutes I am lost, unguided, without compass . . . I let the airplane take its own course, and then, 30 minutes after I left France, I see Deal, which is far to the east of the spot I intended to land upon."

By a single 37-minute flight Bleriot had done more to dramatize the potential of the airplane, for use in war and in peace, than any single man.

"The day that Bleriot flew the Channel marked the end of our insular safety, and the beginning of the time when Britain must seek another form of defense besides its ships," wrote Sir Alan Cobham.

By the same flight that struck such an ominous note in the Europe of 1909, Bleriot assured for himself rich rewards for the efforts of nearly a decade. During this time he had subjected his person to the injuries and pains suffered in some 50 accidents. It is estimated he had spent some $150,000—a very large amount for the period—and some who were in position to know observed that when he undertook the Channel flight, Bleriot was on the verge of bankruptcy.

Now, orders came in from all sides; ultimately they totaled hundreds. The success of Bleriot as a designer and builder of aircraft was assured. In later years, as will be described in another chapter, the monoplane suffered troubles that all but doomed it to extinction for decades, but that in no way detracts from the substantial accomplishments following 1909 by the Bleriot type #11. Bleriot, himself, remained active in aeronautics until his death in 1936. By then, the monoplane was the predominant type, justifying the confidence and energy with which he had carried forward his own efforts.

By 1909 the shape of the airplane had been greatly influenced by the intuitive genius of the French experimenters. Ferber told Chanute he preferred the monoplane to the biplane, because in the air it was the more beautiful. Certainly, no one would accuse the Wright brothers of having produced a thing of beauty. Nor, for that matter, the Voisin Frères, nor Henri Farman or his brother, Maurice. But the Antoinette, and the Bleriot #11, and Esnault-Pelterie's monoplane . . . here were airplanes that not only could fly, on occasion quite tolerably well, but also looked as if that was what their designers had intended.

By their practice of providing a closed body for the pilot—fuselage—the French contributed importantly to the development of the airplane. It was the same, respecting their early preference for the tractor propeller. In the matter of control apparatus, the Bleriot single stick was an example of rational simplicity. At least equally important, was the development of wheeled landing gear by the French. They saw early in the airplane a novel and desirable way to travel from here to there. This being the case, for them the catapult and the landing skid used by the Wrights were *très passé*.

Finally, by way of summing up, the French deserve large credit for developing a method of providing lateral control that was potentially superior to the wing warping of the Wright brothers. No question, especially in the hands of skilled pilots, the lateral control possible from warping of the wings was satisfactory. But warping of the wings meant that, structurally, much was to be desired.

The ailerons, little wings, first used were different from the ailerons of today. In the case of Bleriot's early aircraft, and those of Esnault-Pelterie, the pivoting wing tip offered a means of attaining a measure of lateral stability, but it was not until the idea had been borrowed by the Voisin brothers, that the aileron as we know it today was developed, a hinged flap forming the extreme section of the trailing edge of the wing. As the flap was moved, the airfoil characteristics of the wing itself were changed.

How enthusiastically the French in 1909 had adopted the airplane as their own was to be seen most plainly at the aviation meet held at Rheims in August of that year—as part of the annual champagne week festivities. Some 250,000 spectators were attracted to the aerial show, at which 38 planes were represented. At one time, nine airplanes were in the air.

For the first time, the criticism that the airplane was only a fair-weather plaything was given a dramatic public rebuttal. The pilots flew in storm and winds as high as 25 mph. The meeting at Rheims, more than any other factor, stimulated manufacture of aircraft, not only in France but elsewhere in Europe. At the same time, subsequent events made plain, the demonstrations of the increased range and speed capabilities of the airplane spurred military minds to plan its use as a tool of war.

## WRIGHT VS. VOISIN:

### *Lanchester's Comparison of Two Airplanes*

*The following brief comparison between the Wright Flyer and the biplane built by the Voisin Frères is based upon material contained in a paper Frederick W. Lanchester read on December 8, 1908, to the Aeronautical Society of Great Britain. It is of special interest, more than a half century later, as evidence of how the Wright and Voisin airplanes were evaluated by a knowledgeable contemporary.*

*Lanchester's work will be discussed further in Chapter XIII. He was an automobile manufacturer, an engineer and a mathematician. As early as 1895 he had become interested in the problems of flight, and he did important pioneering work in recognizing and reducing to practical mathematical form some of the basic aerodynamic theories. His* Aerodynamics *and* Aerodonetics, *published in 1907 and 1908, respectively, are considered classics of the early aeronautical literature.*

By way of introduction, Mr. Lanchester observed that: "the most successful types of flying machine or aerodrome at present in existence are those constructed by the Brothers Orville and Wilbur Wright, of the U.S.A., and by MM. Voisin Frères, of Billancourt, Seine, France—on the outskirts of Paris. The author of the present paper has recently had opportunities of witnessing both types of machine in flight, the former at the Champ de Manoeuvres at Champagne, near Le Mans, the latter in the hands of Mr. Farman, over the ground of the military camp at Mourmelon le Grand, near Chalons.

"Although accurate information is on some points difficult to obtain, the reticence shown is perhaps no more than might be anticipated. The author has succeeded in collecting sufficient data to be able to give a consistent account of the performance of both machines, and to permit of an intelligent comparison being made between the two systems."

Lanchester stated that the biplane wings of the Wright machine were 6 ft. apart, and had a span of 41 ft. and a chord of 6½ ft., providing an area of 530 sq. ft. The biplane horizontal elevator extended forward of the wings about 10 ft. and the planes, 2½ ft. apart, measured about 15 by 2½ ft. The planes of the double, vertical steering rudder were 8½ ft. aft of the wings and measured about 6 by 2 ft.

The wings of the Wright airplane were built up from two spars of American spruce, the front spar being about 2 in. thick and located at the leading edge; the second spar was about 4½ ft. aft. The spars had a series of aluminum sockets which held the struts be-between the wings, and wire cross bracing was also used. The ribs of the wings measured 6½ ft., and only those which formed the engine supports were stiff and solid. The trailing edges of the ribs were connected by a steel cable. Fabric of the double-surfaced wings was nailed to the leading edge spar and sewn to the ribs.

The two wooden pusher propellers had 8¼ ft. diameter, and were contrarotating at 450 rpm. Lanchester reported the reduction from the engine crank shaft to the propeller, via chain drive, as being in the ratio of 10 to 33. The propeller shafts were held in brackets, about 11½ ft. apart, supported from the rear of the main frames. He estimated the output of the Wright engine at 24.7 hp.

Weight of the Wright airplane, with pilot, was reported as 1100 lbs., speed as 40 mph., and glide angle as 7°.

The Voisin airplane, according to Lanchester's calculations, had biplane wings about 6¾ ft. apart with a span of about 33 ft. and a chord of 6¾ ft. The two horizontal elevators extended about 4 ft. forward of the wings and were almost on a level with the lower wing. They measured about 7 ft. by 3¼ ft. The tail was of biplane box form and was carried aft of the wings by a 13 ft. outrigger. The span of the horizontal tail planes was about 8 ft. and the chord was about 6¾ ft. The vertical rudder was mounted between the rear main spars of the tail. It was about 4 ft. square.

The two main spars of the Voisin wings were 1½ by ¾ in. in cross section; the forward one was at the leading edge and the other about 5 ft. 6 in. to the rear. Ash ribs of 5/16 by ¾ in. section were 1¼ ft. apart. There were eight pairs of struts between the wings, those at the ends of the wings being farther apart than at the center. Wire cross bracing was also used. Wing surfacing was single.

The single metal pusher propeller had 6½ ft. diameter and was keyed direct to the engine crankshaft. The Antoinette engine was rated at 49.2 hp.

Weight of the Voisin machine, with pilot, was given as 1540 lbs., speed as 45 mph., and glide angle as having been improved from 11° to 9°.

Lanchester noted the Voisin machine was 40 per cent heavier than that of the Wright brothers. After observing that it might be supposed the lesser weight of the Wright airplane was an advantage, he suggested that it might bespeak a more scientific design.

Next he pointed out that the Voisin had a wheeled landing gear, with spring suspension, which improved handling during landing or takeoff on rough ground. He estimated the total weight of this "chassis" at more than 100 lb. The Wright airplane had no such gear, but instead was equipped with "a pair of wooden runners of comparatively little weight."

"If the runners of the Wright machine would do all that can be done by the Voisin mounting, then this additional weight would not be justified," Lanchester said. "But they will not do so; the Voisin machine can rise by itself from any reasonably smooth surface; the Wright is unable to take flight without its [catapult] launching gear, hence it is not legitimate to attribute its relative lightness to the superiority of its design."

Lanchester calculated the efficiency of the Voisin propeller at 54 per cent, compared to 63 per cent efficiency for the Wright propellers, after imposition of a 5 per cent penalty for the Wright chain drive. Efficiency aside, he found the "Voisin system of metal propeller keyed direct to the crankshaft is so immeasurably superior, from the purely *mechanical standpoint*, to the chain drive and wooden propellers of Wright that comparison is unnecessary." Looking ahead, he predicted that "the simplicity of the direct drive may . . . be sufficient to outweigh any economic advantages that gearing may possess."

He went on to observe that in addition to being considerably less efficient in the matter of propellers, "it would appear . . . the Voisin machine is also slightly less efficient considered as a glider, that is to say its gliding angle is not quite so good as that of the Wright machine; the machine is *aerodynamically* less efficient."

Lanchester continued: "The reason for this may be due to the fact that it has a less aspect ratio, but it may quite well also be due to many other causes; the Voisin machine has relatively greater idle surface subject to skin friction, also the sustaining surfaces of the tail act on air that has already been trodden by the aerofoil."

Respecting longitudinal stability, Lanchester said in part: "In the case of the Wright machine it is claimed by Mr. Wright himself that the stability depends entirely on the skill and address of the aeronaut; in fact, if we are to credit the unchallenged account of Mr. Wright's declaration on the subject, he does not believe in the possibility of safety, under ordinary weather conditions, being achieved by the inherent properties of the machine. He says that sooner or later the fatal puff must come that will end the flight . . .

"In the Voisin machine, on the contrary, it has been the intention of the designer that the machine should be automatically and inherently stable . . . the author is at present compelled to speak with some reserve as to the degree of success that MM. Voisin have achieved. . . . There is . . . no proof at present forthcoming as to the stability or otherwise of the flight path of the Voisin machine, but it is at least the intention of the makers that it should be longitudinally stable, and, from conversations that the author has had with MM. Voisin, and with their engineer, M. Colliex, they appear to be alive to many of the points that conduce to such stability."

As to lateral stability, Lanchester observed that "in the Wright machine the lateral stability is under the direct control of the aeronaut," and described as follows how wing-warping operated. "It is desirable to correct a false impression that is current on the action of the wing twist," he continued. "It has been supposed by some that it is used to *give the cant* required by the machine when turning, but such is not the case. If the rudder is used, the machine almost immediately gets a cant owing to the greater pressure on the wing that in turning is moving faster through the air, and this cant becomes, if unchecked, far too severe. The twist is then used to check the cant, the wing on the outer circle—that is, farthest from the center of curvature, being 'feathered,' the inner one having its angle of incidence increased."

Respecting the Voisin machine, Lanchester said, "no hand adjustment is provided to enable the aeronaut to control the lateral stability, hence in this case it is definitely automatic. The Voisin machine is steered by means of a vertical rudder between the fixed tail members, and there is apparently no special mechanism to prevent the over-canting; consequently Farman, in his flights, commonly turns in a leisurely manner, employing a circle of considerable radius, whereas Wright may often be seen to perform sensational evolutions, turning with his wings canted to nearly 30 degs. on a radius of perhaps not more than 60 or 70 yards. Farman has recently had fitted to his machine some adjustable flaps, to give, in effect, the wing twist employed by Wright. Presumably this is to facilitate turning, for the flight of the machine does not suggest that they are otherwise wanted. Under other circumstances the lateral stability leaves little to be desired."

Finally, on the subject of stability and control, Lanchester gave his judgment: "From the *aerodonetic* standpoint (according to Lanchester *aerodonetics* was the science specifically connected with stability or equilibrium of an airplane in flight), the author is inclined to think that the Voisin machine has the advantage, as containing more of the features that will be embodied in the flying machine of the future. Mr. Wright's contention that it only requires a big enough puff of wind to upset a machine that depends upon its inherent stability is certainly true, but probably the same is equally true of the hand-controlled machine. There is a limit to the extent of the control that can be exercised, and with hand control we have, too, the possible failure of the human machine. The fact is that the secret of stability is contained in the one word *velocity*, and until it is possible to attain higher speeds of flight, we cannot hope to see the flying machine in everyday use."

Lanchester made still another comparison: "The constructional methods employed by Wright and Voisin present a striking contrast. The Wright machine is astonishing in its simplicity—not to say apparent crudity of detail—it is almost a matter of surprise that it holds together. The Voisin machine has at least some pretensions to be considered an engineering job.

"Mr. Wright defends his methods by asking what would be said by an engineer to the rigging of a sailing vessel if shown it for the first time, and to some extent the analogy is a good reply to the objection; still the author feels—perhaps wrongly—that there is a considerable amount of the Wright's 'mechanical detail' that might be revised with advantage, at least before the machine is placed in the hands of the private user. However, 'the proof of the pudding is in the eating,' and in spite of the rudimentary character and aggressive simplicity of the constructional detail of the Wright machine, it appears not to come to pieces, but continues to fly day after day without showing any signs of weakness . . ."

# 9/ THE AERIAL EXPERIMENT ASSOCIATION

*The spacious firmament on high,*
*With all the blue ethereal sky,*
*And spangled heavens, a shining frame,*
*Their great Original proclaim.*
*Joseph Addison*

Glenn Hammond Curtiss on June 8, 1911 received aviator's license #1 issued by the Aero Club of America in its capacity (recognized by the Federation Aeronautique Internationale) as the "governing authority for the United States of America." Curtiss, just turned 33, had within the space of three years become world famous as an airplane constructor, as the winner, three times, of the Scientific American trophy, and of the first Gordon Bennett trophy, and as the man who had flown from Albany to New York with only one stop. In other ways he had, no less, shown himself to be in the forefront of the aeronautical pioneers.

It had not always been so. Twice, in the preceding decade, the intense, reserved young man from Upper New York state had shown his main interests to be along different lines from those who sought to fly. For years he had been familiar with the efforts of others to fly, and in fact, he had helped them with the engines he built. But for him, in this time, the path of progress was on the ground. It would not be difficult, especially if one were romantically inclined, to support the thesis that in spite of himself, Glenn Curtiss was pulled inexorably into an aeronautical orbit from which he would not escape for many years.

The early days of Glenn Curtiss fit into the classic mold of an Horatio Alger hero. Left fatherless at the age of five, he was for ten years brought up by a stern if farsighted grandmother. At 15, he began delivering telegrams to support his widowed mother and a younger sister. With only a brief interlude of employment at the Rochester works of the Eastman Kodak company, these and succeeding years were spent in Hammondsport where he undertook, with considerable success, to race, then to repair and sell, and finally, to build bicycles.

From bicycles to motorcycles was a step natural enough to be taken in 1896. Although the first results were disappointing, Curtiss persisted in attempts to build a powerful, reliable engine and an equally rugged cycle frame to carry it. By 1901, his successes on the race track had resulted in enough orders for machines to encourage him to set up a work shop for the manufacture of motorcycles and light, aircooled engines to power them.

In 1903 in a 10-mile race, he won his first national motorcycle championship. In January, 1904, he established a world's record at Ormond Beach, Florida, of 8 minutes, 54 seconds, for the 10-mile distance. In 1907, he sped a measured mile in 26⅖ seconds—136.3 miles per hour. The fact his cycle (powered by an 8-cylinder aircooled engine he had designed and built for an airship) failed to fit into a conventional category and consequently was ineligible for official record-making purposes mattered little. That day, January 23, 1907, Glenn Curtiss traveled faster than man had ever gone, on the earth's surface or above. Not until 1911, when Bob Burman drove a racing automobile 141.7 mph., was his record broken on land; not until World War I neared its end was such speed attained in the air.

By 1903—to introduce the first of two men who were to exert greatest aeronautical influence upon Glenn Curtiss—Capt. Thomas Scott Baldwin had already been active as a balloonist and parachute jumper for nearly a quarter century. Baldwin's 1903 goal was to follow the example set by Santos-Dumont in 1901, to construct a powered, steerable airship. Located in California, Capt. Baldwin came across a Curtiss-built motorcycle and was so impressed by its two-cylinder engine that he ordered forthwith a special powerplant—a 2-cylinder aircooled engine of 5 hp.—for his "California Arrow." Lack of operating capital rather than difficulty of production held up construction and delivery of the new Curtiss engine for months, but finally it was installed in Baldwin's airship which, in August 1904 at Oakland, Calif., was the first in America to fly in a circle.

So far as Glenn Curtiss was concerned, special-order manufacture of engines to power slow-flying airships was interesting, profitable business but little more. In succeeding years he built a number, for Baldwin and others, but for the long pull he preferred to concentrate upon his motorcycle manufacturing business.

In 1907—to introduce the man who was himself an aeronautical pioneer and who finally succeeded more than anyone in interesting Curtiss in aeronautics as a challenge surpassing all others—Dr. Alexander Graham Bell invited the Hammondsport manufacturer (not yet 30) to make personal delivery of an engine for aircraft use to the Bell summer home at Beinn Breagh, on Lake Bras d'Or near Baddeck, Nova Scotia.

To make his invitation the more attractive, Dr. Bell offered to pay Curtiss $25 per day plus expenses. He had met Curtiss in the winter of 1905–06, and in fact, on that occasion he had placed an order for an engine to be used in connection with his aerial experiments. After more than a year had passed without delivery, he visited Curtiss at Hammondsport. The first engine Curtiss built was too heavy for its power, and it was in connection with delivery of a second that the invitation was given.

Dr. Bell's interest in aeronautics was no passing fancy. In a paper, "Aerial Locomotion," read to the Washington Academy of Sciences, December 13, 1906, he recalled:—"For many years past, in fact from my boyhood, the subject of aerial flight has had a great fascination for me. Before the year 1896 I had made many thousands of still unpublished experiments having a bearing upon the subject; and I was therefore much interested in the researches of Professor Langley relating to aerodynamics . . . [Dr. Bell was a Regent of the Smithsonian; Prof. Langley was Secretary of the Institution.] At least as early as 1894, Professor Langley visited me in my Nova Scotia home and witnessed some of my experiments; and in May, 1896 he reciprocated by inviting me to accompany him to Quantico, Virginia, and witness a trial of his large sized model. [*See Chapter*

*IV*.] The sight of Langley's steam aerodrome circling in the sky convinced me that the age of flying machine was at hand."

The approach taken by the inventor of the telephone was calculated to save life and limb. "Should an accident happen to a body propelled through the air with the velocity of a railroad train, how about the safety of the occupants?" Dr. Bell asked. To minimize such dangers, he chose to fly his aerial vehicles as kites, and to conduct his experiments over water.

(As told in Chapters VII and VIII, Cody and Hargrave conducted experiments with kites in England and Australia, respectively. In North America, too, others were working with kites. For example, the *Scientific American* reported in its November, 1905 issue:

"The latest of the aeronautic experiments of Israel Ludlow, of New York City, occurred on Sunday, October 22, when the aeroplane carrying Charles K. Hamilton, a professional aeronaut, was successfully launched into the air from the east bank of the Hudson River, and after a flight of some minutes' duration, settled gradually into the water near midstream. The experiment was intended thoroughly to test the flying, or more properly the gliding, properties of the machine, and for this purpose the motive power at the end of the rope, or 'kite string,' was a powerful tugboat, an arrangement permitting the use as a course the unbroken sweep above the river. After a number of unsuccessful starts—the slack not being completely taken up before the drag acted on the machine—the aeroplane was at length flung into the air in the teeth of a strong wind. Until a height of approximately 500 feet was attained the rise was rather erratic; Hamilton, however, with great coolness, managed to keep the giant white-winged kite on an even keel by shifting his weight from one point to another as the occasion required, and when more than 600 feet of rope had been let out from the tugboat, the machine settled down and followed the wake of the vessel.")

In discussing his experiment, Dr. Bell was quick to note that "the word 'kite' unfortunately is suggestive to most minds of a toy—just as the telephone at first was thought to be a toy—so that the word does not at all adequately express the nature of the enormous flying structures employed in some of my experiments . . . These were really aerial vehicles rather than kites, for they were capable of lifting men and heavy weights into the air."

He was aware of the square-cube law which the mathematician Prof. Simon Newcomb in 1901 had decided would delay "construction of an aerial vehicle which could carry even a single man from place to place at pleasure (until) the discovery of some new metal or some new force." He conceded "a small bird could not sustain a heavy load in the air; and that it is true that a bird of double the dimensions would be able to carry a less proportionate weight because it is heavier in proportion to its wing surface than the smaller bird—eight times as heavy, with only four times the wing surface."

Dr. Bell then suggested his own answer to this dilemma:—"It is conceivable that a small flock of birds could sustain a heavy load divided equally among them." In this case, he reasoned, "the ratio of weight to wing surface would be the same for the whole flock as for the individual bird."

His solution, translated into structural form, was the tetrahedron —in which the skeleton frame was composed of six rods of equal length to outline a solid form bounded by four equal triangular faces. Two of the faces were covered with silk or waterproof Japanese paper to form a Vee. When Dr. Bell connected a series of tetrahedral cells by their corners, he found the resulting structure possessed remarkable rigidity, plus "the same properties of strength and lightness inherent in the individual cells themselves." He was greatly pleased by the inherent stability it demonstrated.

In late December, 1905, his "Frost King" was successfully flown. By no means the largest of the tetrahedral kites he would construct, it was made up of 1,300 silk-surfaced cells arranged in 12 layers. At least once it lifted into the air a total of 227 pounds—62 lbs. of rope and rope ladder as well as a 165-lb. man—in addition to its own weight of 61 lbs.

The next summer, 1906, Dr. Bell decided to build a larger kite along the same lines, this one to be equipped with an engine. That summer he was aided in his work by two young Canadians, John A. Douglas McCurdy and Frederick W. "Casey" Baldwin. McCurdy, an engineering student at Toronto University, had just turned 20; his father had been Dr. Bell's secretary and had assisted in his earlier aeronautical experiments. Baldwin, no relation to Capt. Baldwin, the balloonist, was a grandson of one of the men who had united the Provinces of Canada into the Dominion. Nearing 30, he had that year received his engineering degree from Toronto. So engrossing did their labors become that they both remained at Beinn Breagh throughout the winter.

In the spring of 1907, they were joined by a lieutenant in the 5th Field Artillery of the U.S. Army, Thomas E. Selfridge. A graduate of West Point, Selfridge for many months had been interested in aviation. He had availed himself of the extensive collection of aeronautical literature available in the Library of Congress in Washington, and had read widely from the literature, including works in French, German, and Italian. When, in August, Brig. Gen. James Allen, Chief Signal Officer, established an Aeronautical Division within the Army Signal Corps with Capt. Charles DeForest Chandler in charge, Lieut. Selfridge was assigned to duty in the Division. (Soon, Lieut. Frank P. Lahm reported for duty under Capt. Chandler, to be joined not long after by Lieut. Benjamin D. Foulois.) "Suggestions" were made—according to one account to President William Howard Taft—and Lieut. Selfridge was detailed in the early fall to return to Nova Scotia to study aeronautics.

These, then, were the men with whom Curtiss worked in Nova Scotia. Their unquestioned leader was Dr. Bell. Now 60, he wore a great white beard; it gave him a mild, patriarchal appearance that belied the vistas of his soaring thoughts. Perhaps it was the willingness of the experimenters to pay him well for his services that caused Curtiss to remain at Beinn Breagh. More likely, it was the inspiration that came from listening to the conversations that lasted far into the night and told so well of the pioneering efforts of other talented men around the world. At any rate, when he was asked to join formally in further aeronautical pioneering, Curtiss agreed.

It was Mrs. Bell who suggested the idea and provided the funds necessary for establishment and operation of the Aerial Experiment Association. Articles of agreement were drawn and signed September 30, 1907. Therein, it was stated that Dr. Bell had called upon the others for assistance in bringing to a logical conclusion his work to build a man-carrying, powered airship on the tetrahedral principle. Further, it was noted that the others had independent ideas respecting aerial locomotion which he would assist them to pursue. Working together, "individually and conjointly," their common purpose was "to get into the air." Dr. Bell was chairman; Curtiss, executive officer and director of experiments; "Casey" Baldwin, chief engineer; McCurdy, assistant engineer and treasurer, and Selfridge, secretary.

First of the Aerial Experiment Association's projects was construction of Cygnet I (baby swan). Built from some 3,000 silk and wood tetrahedral cells, it was to be man-carrying and to be powered by a Curtiss engine. By December, it was ready for the first flight tests on Bras d'Or Lake, to be made without power. Placed aboard a scow, with Selfridge the "pilot," it was towed into the wintry wind and soon became airborne. For some 7 minutes, during which Cygnet I reached a height calculated to be 178 feet, Selfridge soared through the air.

His vehicle had no controls; even the procedure whereby it was to be freed from the tow rope was left to a workman on the towing steamer. This latter condition was responsible for the dreary condition of the Cygnet I at the end of the flight. As the wind lessened, the kite sank lower and lower until it touched the water. All might have been well if the workman, perhaps bemused by the wonder of what he saw, had remembered to wield his axe and sever the tow rope. As it was, Cygnet I was pulled roughly through the waters—not for long but long enough to shred its fragile structure beyond hope of repair. Despite the icy wetting, Selfridge suffered no harm. Dr. Bell was not discouraged. A larger tetrahedral kite, Cygnet II, was planned, and would be completed in 1909. Except for rapid progress made along other lines in the time intervening, the effort to advance Dr. Bell's theories might have been accelerated.

Previously, plans had been undertaken for an airplane which Curtiss was to construct. Now, as 1907 drew to a close, the Association made two important decisions. A glider would be built first, to enable gaining the experience in motorless flight that Selfridge suggested would be so valuable later, and operations would be shifted for the winter to Hammondsport. No question, there would still be snow and cold aplenty, but the advantages of working with the Curtiss machine shop close by were persuasive. During the early weeks of 1908, all members of the A.E.A. except Dr. Bell took turns learning to fly the Chanute-type biplane glider. Even though the slopes they chose were fairly abrupt, a wind of 15-mph velocity was necessary for reasonably successful hops.

Meantime, the first of four powered airplanes planned was being built. Called the Red Wing, its biplane design was Selfridge's responsibility, although all Association members felt free to make suggestions. The engine was aircooled and had 8 cylinders; bore was 3⅝ inches and stroke 3¼ inches, developing, hopefully, about 25 horsepower. The pusher propeller was metal. The wings, with spars and ribs made of spruce, were covered with a single surface of red silk and had a span of 43 feet. They were tapered from a width of about 6 feet at the center to 4 feet at the wing tips; total lifting surface was 380 square feet. An elevator, located forward, measured 8 x 2 feet, while the rudder, aft, was 4 feet square. No provisions were made for lateral control.

Because Selfridge had been called to Washington by military responsibilities in March when the Red Wing was ready for its trials (Dr. Bell, too, was away from Hammondsport at the time) "Casey" Baldwin was chosen pilot by lot. On March 12, the Red Wing, equipped with runners, was pushed out onto the ice of Lake Keuka. After a run of some 250 feet, it rose into the air and covered a distance of 318 feet, never higher than 8 feet, before it landed heavily on the ice. It was later determined that the airplane had stalled, falling off on one wing. The tail structure was smashed, and other damage was done, but Baldwin escaped serious injury. Although this flight followed the December 17, 1903 efforts of Wilbur and Orville Wright by more than four years, the manner in which it was undertaken and the location of the effort caused it to be described as the first *public* flight by an airplane in America.

Rather than attempt repair of the Red Wing, construction of the second airplane was begun. Because an undyed fabric was used to cover the surfaces, it was named the White Wing; Baldwin was responsible for its design.

Achievement of lateral control was, of course, imperative if the efforts of the Aerial Experiment Association were to prove genuinely fruitful. In a letter written to Baldwin on March 20, Dr. Bell discussed the problem at length, and then proposed the means by which the problem could be solved. Why not, he suggested, make the wing tips moveable, with the controls so arranged that when one tip was elevated, the other would be depressed by an equal amount. Whether Dr. Bell was at the time aware of the similarity between his suggestion and the lateral-control devices used as early as 1904 by Esnault-Pelterie and 1907 by Bleriot (*See Chapter VIII*) is not known. Another possibility, of course, is that Dr. Bell's proposal might have been occasioned by his awareness of the wing-warping technique of the Wright brothers. In 1908, as secretary of the A.E.A., Selfridge had requested information from the Wrights and had been referred to their U.S. patents, issued in 1906. Be that as it may, Dr. Bell's ideas were incorporated—together with a shoulder yoke to make them virtually automatic—in the design of the White Wing.

Numerous other changes were made in the design and construction of the White Wing as compared to the Red Wing, but for the most part these were minor. Because flight tests would be made in warmer weather, motorcycle wheels were used instead of the original ice runners. Between May 18 and May 23, 1908 all A.E.A. members except Dr. Bell made flights in the White Wing. The longest, a distance of 1,017 feet, was made by Curtiss. The last, some 600 feet with McCurdy the pilot, resulted in a smashup. Selfridge's earlier flight had marked him as the first U.S. Army officer to pilot an airplane.

In a very real sense the Aerial Experiment Association was making rapid progress. Its first two airplanes had gotten into the air. Its members, self taught, were learning how to fly. The Red Wing and White Wing accidents were the sort of mishap that any experimenter of the period expected as a certain cost of his pioneering.

Gratifying as this progress must have been, there was no room for complacency. Although the Wright brothers had made their flights in private, their statements about having remained airborne for longer than a half hour at a time and over distances of almost 25 miles were accepted as fact by Dr. Bell and his associates. Too, the Wrights had undertaken to build a "flyer" for the War Department capable of carrying two passengers at 40 mph. for at least an hour nonstop, a development Selfridge must have known. In Europe, flights had been made publicly over distances greater than those managed in the White Wing. (*See Chapters* VI *and* VIII.)

Awareness of the accelerating pace of aeronautics fully as much as the size of the task of rebuilding the White Wing spurred the A.E.A. to construction of its third airplane. Although the changes made in design were ones largely of detail, i.e., the control system for the moveable wing tips was simplified and improved, the net result was an airplane which gave markedly better performance. The same engine was used as before because an improved power plant was not finished in time. Wooden skids, placed above the wheels, protected the plane from serious damage in the event of landing gear failure. Responsibility for the new craft was given to Curtiss. Although he lacked the engineering training of his associates, his years of experimenting with cycles and engines, learning how to build them more powerful and make them more reliable, had given him the special talents that often enabled him to determine what had to be done to transform failure into success—plus the ingenuity to accomplish the necessary changes.

Christened June Bug at the suggestion of Dr. Bell, the A.E.A.'s third airplane made its first flight on June 20, 1908, with Curtiss the pilot, and covered 1,266 feet. In the days that followed, other Association members flew greater distances, and on July 4, Curtiss flew 5,090 feet in one minute 42⅕ seconds to win the Scientific American trophy, administered by the Aero Club of America, for the first public flight of more than one kilometer in America. Perhaps even more important than the trophy flight of the June Bug was the accomplishment, first only partial by McCurdy and later complete by Curtiss, of a 180° turn in flight. In addition to their efforts to fly farther, they were learning how to maneuver. Again, they were following the lead of others but the gap was being closed.

Now, the A.E.A. group became engaged in a number of diverse activities, both as Association members and as individuals concerned with private interests. Curtiss spent much time on construction of an airship engine, about which more later. After staying at Hammondsport most of the summer working with McCurdy and Curtiss on the fourth airplane to be built, Selfridge was called to Washington early in September to serve as a member of the Army's Aeronautical Board, established to witness the tests of the airplane built by the Wright brothers. Baldwin went to Nova Scotia, to work with Dr. Bell on tetrahedral structures and also on waterborne craft.

September 17, 1908, Lieut. Thomas Selfridge was killed in the crash of the Wright Flyer at Fort Myer, Va. Only 26 at the time, he had been a valued member of the Aerial Experiment Association. His loss was deeply felt, and caused the group to consider whether the Association should be continued beyond its first year. The decision was in the affirmative. There was work to be done, and Mrs. Bell's offer of additional financial assistance, enough to last through March of 1909, was accepted.

The June Bug, now fitted with twin floats and renamed the Loon, was tested as a water-based craft early in December. When, with Curtiss at the controls, it refused to become airborne, a more powerful engine was fitted, but still it failed to take to the air. Finally, when the Loon sank in shallow water after damage to one of the floats, the experiments with this, the Association's third and best known airplane, were concluded.

Silver Dart was the name of the A.E.A.'s fourth airplane. Powered by a 35 hp., 8-cylinder engine driving a geared pusher propeller, it was McCurdy's project and represented a considerable advance over earlier work by the group. Its wings, covered with gray, rubberized silk, tapered from 6 feet at midsection to 4 feet, exclusive of the wing tips. Wing span was 49 feet, including the tips, and wing area was 420 square feet. Loaded weight, including pilot, was about 800 pounds. First flown at Hammondsport in December, it was shipped to Baddeck the following month, and on February 23, 1909, McCurdy traveled more than a half mile in the first airplane flight to be made in Canada. In fact, his performance was recognized as the first by a British subject anywhere in the Commonwealth. The next month, McCurdy flew the Silver Dart nonstop a distance of 20 miles.

In February and March, 1909, also, the Association conducted its final experiments, using the new Cygnet II. Composed of 3,690 tetrahedral cells, it was mounted on steel runners and equipped with controls. Carrying the Silver Dart's engine and a pilot, it weighed 950 lbs. On its first flight, the propeller broke; on later attempts it failed to pick up sufficient speed to get into the air.

On March 31, 1909, the Aerial Experiment Association ceased to exist. Dr. Bell was disappointed that the tetrahedral structures he favored had failed to fulfill their promise. On the other hand, he and Mrs. Bell had every reason to be gratified by the great progress made by their young associates. In dissolving the Association, it was agreed that Curtiss would hold American rights to the aeronautical improvements its members had made.

McCurdy and "Casey" Baldwin shared similar rights in Canada. For two years they sought unsuccessfully to interest the Canadian government in the airplane. They made numerous flights both in the Silver Dart and later in their Baddeck I and II, to no avail. In 1910, "Casey" Baldwin turned to other interests, while McCurdy continued active flying until about 1916, and resumed his association with Curtiss for part of that time. In a later chapter, his name will reappear.

# 10/ GLENN H. CURTISS

*We judge ourselves by what we feel*
*capable of doing*
*While others judge us by what we*
*have already done.*
HENRY WADSWORTH LONGFELLOW

During the brief but fruitful existence of the Aerial Experiment Association—September 30, 1907 to March 31, 1909—(*See Chapter IX*) its most vigorous member, Glenn H. Curtiss, continued to operate his G. H. Curtiss Manufacturing Company at Hammondsport, N.Y., producing motorcycles and special-order engines.

In 1908, for example, he contracted to design and build a more powerful engine for a new dirigible Capt. Thomas Baldwin was constructing for the US Army. To assist in the design, which represented a departure from the air-cooled engines he previously manufactured, Curtiss employed A. L. Pfitzner, an Hungarian engineer. For five months or longer the Curtiss shop labored to produce the 24-hp., 4-cylinder, aluminum-jacketed, water-cooled powerplant which was finally evolved.

When installed, it proved to be capable of continuous operation for two hours or longer. In August of that year, Capt. Baldwin gave the required performance demonstrations, and Curtiss accompanied him on the flights. While the former operated the controls, the latter kept the engine running. Top speed of the airship was almost 20 mph. In these years, too, Curtiss engines were built to power other airships, and one was installed in a helicopter J. Newton Williams, a Connecticut typewriter manufacturer, had built and brought to Hammondsport.

In the early months of 1909, even before dissolution of the Aerial Experiment Association, Glenn Curtiss began negotiations with Augustus M. Herring which led that spring to formation of the Herring-Curtiss Company to manufacture airplanes. Cortlandt Field Bishop, president of the Aero Club of America, also was interested in the new company. Doubtless, Curtiss felt proud to join forces with an aeronautical pioneer so well known as Herring; his new associate had experimented with gliders in the 90's and for a brief time had worked with Octave Chanute. Of the corporation difficulties which soon arose, or of the litigation which followed concerning the alleged infringement on the Wright patents by the Curtiss lateral control system, little need be said here except to note that legal proceedings on both matters would continue for many years.

The first airplane construction by Curtiss, independent of the Aerial Experiment Association, was the Gold Bug, built to order of the Aeronautical Society of New York. The price was $5,000. After having been delivered, it was loaned back to Curtiss who, on July 17, 1909, flew it 24.7 miles nonstop to win the Scientific American trophy for the second straight year.

Although it generally resembled the June Bug, the Gold Bug was smaller, with a weight of hardly 550 lbs., and it differed in important detail. The moveable wing tips, by now commonly called ailerons, had been removed. In their place, winglets 2 x 6 feet for lateral control were mounted outboard between the biplane wings. The wings themselves were no longer tapered; they measured 28 feet 9 inches by 4 feet 6 inches and were 5 feet apart. The wings were single surfaced and the rubberized silk used was attached to the ribs by tightly drawn pockets.

Two outriggers extended 12 feet fore and aft. In front were the biplane elevators measuring 2 x 6 feet. Between the elevators and extending above the upper surface was a triangular vertical "prow" which gave improved directional stability. To the rear were the horizontal tail and rudder, measuring 12 and 6¼ square feet, respectively.

The controls included a steering wheel and a shoulder yoke. Turning the wheel worked the rudder; pushing it in and out on a sliding shaft operated the elevators. By moving his shoulders against the yoke, the pilot operated the ailerons.

The frame was made from selected spruce. The engine bed and the tricycle landing gear structure were also made of wood. Two of the 20-inch diameter wheels were at the trailing edge of the wings while the third was mounted on the fore outrigger. Bamboo was used extensively in construction of the outriggers.

The 4-cylinder water-cooled engine was rated at 30 hp. at 1,200 rpm. Copper water jackets were used. With radiator, Bosch magneto, etc., the engine weight was 192 lbs. The six-foot diameter pusher propeller was bolted directly to the crankshaft.

Even before winning the Scientific American trophy, Curtiss was building another airplane for use in the first Gordon Bennett trophy speed contest to be held late in August in France. In essence, the differences between the Golden Flyer and its predecessor, the Gold Bug, were those of adding power and saving every possible ounce of weight. An 8-cylinder, water-cooled engine, rated at 50 hp., was built; so close was the margin of time before the airplane had to be shipped from Hammondsport that the engine testing was limited to a single day's running on the test block. The propeller was larger, with a seven-foot diameter.

The wings, dimensioned the same as those of the Gold Bug, were constructed in sections to facilitate disassembly and shipment. They had 22 laminated spruce ribs. Bracing was by woven cable instead of the piano wire commonly used, and the control wires were passed through bamboo tubes to prevent chafing.

On August 28, 1909, on the Bethany plains outside Rheims, the week-long, first International Aviation Meet was climaxed by the Gordon Bennett trophy event. Chief competitors were Louis Bleriot, darling of France for his Channel crossing of the previous month, and Curtiss. The day before Louis Paulhan had flown nonstop 118 miles in 3¼ hours. Now the criterion would be speed, two laps around a 10-km. course. Curtiss flew first, averaging 47.04 mph., but Bleriot, using a new 80 hp. engine in his monoplane, was favored. His first leg was 5⅖ seconds better than Curtiss had managed. On his second lap, Bleriot faltered, and his total time was 5⅗ seconds slower than the 15 minutes, 50⅗ seconds time by Curtiss. The young man from Upper New York state had become world famous for his aeronautical prowess no less than for his motorcycling exploits. Now, he was the fastest man in the world, both in the skies and on the ground.

The next year, May 29, 1910, Curtiss made more aeronautical history, this time by flying, with only a single stop for fuel, the 150 miles between Albany and New York, to win the $10,000 prize offered by the *New York World.* The airplane he flew was similar to the Golden Flyer except for the simple precautions he had taken to keep his aircraft afloat in the event of an emergency landing in the Hudson river.

A tube of rubberized cloth, filled with cork, was stretched fore and aft along the framework of the landing gear. A small hydrofoil was fitted to the front of the tube to guard against capsizing. Metal flotation tanks were also attached to the wing tips. Total weight of the Albany Flyer was about 1,000 lbs. Time in the air was 2 hours 51 minutes, for an average speed of 52.6 mph. The first leg, 87 miles, won for Curtiss the Scientific American trophy for the third year, thus entitling him to its permanent possession.

Now one comes to a phase of Glenn Curtiss' work which well may stand as his most important aeronautical contribution—his pioneering developments in marine aviation. Water as the ideal surface for airplane takeoffs and landings was no idea exclusive to Curtiss. As early as 1901, Wilhelm Kress in Austria had sought, unsuccessfully, to fly a seaplane. (*See Chapter VII.*) In France, too, water-based, launch-towed gliders had been used by early experimenters.

As a matter of fact, the honor of having been the first to take off from and land on water belongs to a Frenchman, as will be detailed presently, but it was not until 1911 when Glenn Curtiss finally succeeded in developing a water-based airplane that marine aviation got its real start.

In the fall of 1908, the June Bug had been fitted with twin floats (actually little more than covered canoes) by Curtiss and the other members of the Aerial Experiment Association. (*See Chapter IX.*) Renamed the Loon, it refused to become airborne even when a more powerful engine was installed.

It was Henri Fabre, in 1910, who made the first landings and takeoffs from water. His accomplishment was from the Bay of Martiques, near Marseilles, and his aircraft was a canard monoplane with a wing area of 280 square feet. The three hollow flexibly-mounted floats, one forward and two aft under the wing, were relatively flat on the bottom and shaped like an airfoil. The 50-hp. Gnome-rotary engine drove a Chauvière pusher propeller. Adding to the strange appearance of Fabre's monoplane was the construction of the single wing spar; it was made of two ash planks eight inches wide and ¼ inch thick with triangular trussing made up of flat steel plates. Fabre's seat straddled one of two beams which extended forward from the wing to the control surfaces. On March 28, he made a flight of about a third of a mile, never rising more than a few feet off the water. On May 17, he made another water takeoff, this time flying a distance of more than 3 miles, but his landing was made at too steep an angle and the hydroplane was badly damaged.

Curtiss, during 1910, took a different approach to the problem of developing an airplane for naval use. What he was attempting was to answer affirmatively the question posed by Capt. W. Irving Chambers, USN, whether airplanes could be launched from and landed on ships. The first trials were scheduled to be made November 5 by J. A. D. McCurdy, by now back with Curtiss, from a platform erected on the stern of a steamer of the Hamburg-American Line as it sailed from New York harbor. First, foul weather caused a cancellation, and then after other delays, the plane's propeller was damaged during warmup on the 12th. Meanwhile, perhaps unhappy at the prospect of naval aviation history being made from a German vessel, Capt. Chambers had obtained the use of the *USS Birmingham*, and on November 14th another Curtiss pilot, Eugene Ely, took off from the cruiser at the mouth of Chesapeake Bay. The plane had insufficient forward speed when it ran off the deck and dropped so low some observers thought the wheels might have touched the water. But Ely kept flying and landed on Willoughby Spit, near Norfolk.

On January 19, 1911, Ely brought the experiment to a successful conclusion, landing his Curtiss biplane on a 125-foot platform on the aft deck of the *USS Pennsylvania* in San Francisco Bay. The arresting gear consisted of hooks on the airplane and 22 lines across the platform, each anchored by a pair of 50-pound sand bags. Later in the day, Ely made another takeoff from shipboard.

What was really wanted, Secretary of the Navy George von L. Meyer had made plain, was an airplane that could take off and land on water, and be taken aboard ship, or lowered, by a boat crane. Curtiss endeavored to build a craft with precisely those capabilities. Construction of the necessary floats was at Hammondsport; the efforts to take off from the water so equipped were in a standard Curtiss biplane off North Island at San Diego, Cal., where Curtiss had established a flying school. Much of the early marine work by Curtiss was strictly cut-and-try. His experiments had convinced him that use of displacement-hull type of floats would not do. It was possible to accelerate along the water to a fair rate of speed, using long, narrow floats, but the airplane so equipped showed no inclination to become airborne. Next, Curtiss tried a main pontoon, two feet wide and eight feet long, with a shovel nose and a flat bottom. But even the addition of a third wing, to provide more lift, failed to give the solution. Before he succeeded, on January 26, 1911, in becoming "unstuck" from the waters of San Diego Bay, as many as 50 combinations of float shape, size and location were tried.

The configuration Curtiss used on his first successful flight from the water incorporated a large float 6 feet wide, 7 feet from front to rear, and 10 inches thick at the deepest part. The bottom was flat and angled downward from the front about 10°. Forward, at about the same position of the front wheel of the land machine, was a second float 6 feet wide, 1 foot from front to rear, and 6 inches at the deepest part. A small elevating hydrovane with a spray shield was positioned at the extreme front on an outrigger. Air-filled skis, 4 feet long, were suspended from the wing tips.

Once he learned how to make a water takeoff, Curtiss proceeded in characteristic fashion to simplify. Now he used a single float, 12 feet long, 2 feet wide, and 1 foot deep. Weighing only 50 pounds, compared to almost 100 pounds for the two fore-and-aft floats previously used, it most resembled in appearance a flat-bottomed scow. First trials on February 1 were successful, and by the 17th, Curtiss was ready to demonstrate that his craft could satisfy naval requirements. Taking off from the water, he flew across San Diego Bay and alighted near the *Pennsylvania,* where his plane was hoisted aboard. After congratulations had been exchanged and the amenities observed, the airplane was lowered over the side, and Curtiss took off on his return flight to North Island.

The obvious satisfaction with which the Navy viewed these latest demonstrations seemed to spur Curtiss to further experimentation and improvement. A second seaplane was constructed, this time using a tractor propeller instead of the usual pusher. Disliking the propeller blast in his face, Curtiss quickly returned to the previous propeller arrangement.

On February 23 he made a successful flight in what has been called the world's first amphibian. All Curtiss had done was to fit his seaplane with tricycle landing gear, with a simple lever arrangement which permitted lowering the wheels for landing or takeoff on ground, and raising them for operation from water. The Navy's first plane purchase included one of this type, called Triad because it could operate from land or sea and in the air. (The Navy bought three airplanes in 1911, the Triad, a Curtiss land plane, and a Wright land plane.)

Lt. Theodore G. Ellyson (the first Navy pilot) and Lt. John H. Towers (who will be long remembered for his many contributions to naval aviation) made history in the Triad. On October 11, 1911, they took off from Annapolis—where a Navy airfield had been built at Greenbury Point—and headed for Old Point Comfort. After about a half hour, they were forced to come down by a broken safety wire on the gas tank. Another 20 minutes in the air, and the failure of a carburetor bracket again forced them down. Thirty flying minutes later, engine bearings burned out, forcing cancellation of the flight, 79 miles from home. The next attempt succeeded, on October 25, with the Triad making the 147 miles to Buckroe Beach, adjacent to Old Point, nonstop in 2 hours, 27 minutes. This, despite a leaking radiator hose connection which Towers had to hold in place for more than an hour of flight. Not long after, Lt. Towers made a duration flight of 6 hours, 10 minutes, 35 seconds, in a Curtiss seaplane—a world's record for a hydroplane and an American record regardless of type.

Curtiss was agreeable, Ellyson and Towers soon found, to trying out all sorts of new ideas. He accepted their suggestion for a dual control system, perhaps patterned after French practice, and with modification this arrangement became standard on Navy training planes. Perhaps the most spectacular experiment so inspired was the effort to devise an arrangement of wires whereby a seaplane could be launched from shipboard. Tested at Hammondsport in September, 1911, with Ellyson the pilot, the rig actually worked, but it was obvious that it was impractical for service use.

In brief, the launching system made use of a main wire or cable, with two auxiliary wires. A groove, lined with metal, was cut along the centerline of the main float, so the craft would slide down the wire. The auxiliary wires were arranged to keep the wings from tipping while launching. "Everything happened so quickly and went off so smoothly that I hardly know what happened except that I did have to use the ailerons," Ellyson wrote Capt. Chambers, "I am not making an official report of this experiment."

In 1912, Ellyson was pilot during launching tests utilizing a compressed-air catapult which Capt. Chambers, Naval Constructor Holden C. Richardson, and Lt. St. Clair Smith of the Naval Gun Factory had devised. On July 31, the experiment ended in a badly damaged airplane dumped into the Severn river at Annapolis, but by November Richardson's improvements to the catapult enabled successful takeoffs. So far as Curtiss was concerned, the catapult was the most important device since the advent of wheels on land planes.

Even before the end of 1911, Curtiss had undertaken development of a flying boat—instead of hooking pontoons on to what was essentially a land plane, he wished to install wings, engine and propeller in a true boat hull. In this effort a series of failures preceded success.

In its original form, the Curtiss flying boat hull was flat-bottomed and of the same general shape as the seaplane pontoon, but considerably larger. The engine, located in the bow in front of the pilot, powered two tractor propellers through a chain drive. First trials, on San Diego Bay, were uniformly unsuccessful despite numerous modifications. On January 10, 1912, Curtiss became airborne in his flying boat, but this achievement served only to increase his belief that from the hydrodynamic standpoint, something more suitable than the flat-bottom hull certainly was required. So, that spring, the flying boat was shipped to Hammondsport for major changes (not the least of which was moving the engine back between the wings, to drive a single pusher propeller) and more experimentation on Lake Keuka.

But the flying boat refused to become unstuck from the lake, and fly. Refused, that is, until the question was asked, "Why not put blocks on the bottom of the hull to make a step? Perhaps that way, the suction aft on the hull could be broken up." Whether Naval Constructor Richardson who spent some time at Hammondsport, asked the question of Curtiss, or vice versa, is not too important. The step was built; the flying boat became unstuck, and flew.

In the form it was built in some numbers, both for domestic customers (mostly well-to-do sportsmen) and for foreign purchasers, the Curtiss flying boat had a hull 26 feet long, 3 feet wide, and 3 feet deep, with a single hydroplane step along the otherwise flat bottom. The biplane wings measured 30 by 5½ feet, providing about 320 square feet of wing surface, allowing for cutouts. Interplane ailerons were used. The Curtiss Model O V-8 water-cooled engine was rated at 80 hp.

Horizontal and vertical "rudders" were used at the tail, and for the first time, Curtiss dispensed with a front elevator. Inclined cylindrical floats were fitted below the ends of the lower wing, in case the flying boat tipped during landing or in making a quick turn when taxiing.

As a consequence of his naval aviation work, Glenn Curtiss received the Collier trophy, for his "hydroaeroplane" of 1911, and for his flying boat of 1912. These were the first two presentations of this premier aviation award. Many other honors ultimately were his, including the Langley Gold Medal of the Smithsonian Institution in 1913, for his marine aviation pioneering.

Beginning in 1912, another important step forward was undertaken. With Curtiss in Europe, his superintendent of engine production headed a drive to get more power from the 80 hp. Model O. Almost any gain would have been welcomed; before the modifications had been completed the following year, dynamometer tests showed the Model O to be producing a maximum of 105 hp. Originally called the O plus, the plus sign was mistakenly changed to an X, and it later became world famous as the OX 5 which powered the World War I Jenny.

Curtiss had made the first *public* flights in the United States in 1908, and by virtue of his performance, received license #1 from the Aero Club of America in 1911. Now, four years after his first flights, numerous officers in both the Army and the Navy were becoming aware both of the potential military value of the airplane, and also of the disquieting fact that in Europe, development of the airplane for military purposes was progressing much faster than in the United States. Lack of interest in high official quarters and, even more serious, lack of anything but token sums for airplane procurement were providing effective brakes on airplane development effort.

Even so, progress was being made in America. Its extent can be judged by the scope of the requirements of the Army and Navy in 1912, as outlined in the invitations to offer airplanes to satisfy the pitifully small procurement programs of that year.

Specifications issued by the Navy for hydro-airplanes stipulated as a full load, two passengers with a combined weight of 350 pounds, plus necessary wireless gear and other instruments. Maximum speed was to be at least 55 mph., while 50 mph. was the acceptable minimum for the required 4-hour nonstop flight with full load. Takeoff from the water under still-air conditions had to be with a run of no more than 1,000 feet. Air-cooled engines would be preferred. The planes were to be so constructed as to permit their being hoisted intact aboard ship, and to be capable of quick disassembly. They were to be seaworthy, with engine dead, in the face of 20-mile winds.

For its part, the Army announced the intention of buying and using only two types of airplane. The first, to be known as the Speed Scout, was to be a single-seater which would be used for strategical reconnaissance. Its speed was to be not less than 65 mph., with a range of about 100 miles and climbing capability of 600 feet per minute. Called the Scout, the second type was to be a two-seater with dual controls and was to be equipped with radio. Its speed capabilities were a minimum of 45 mph. and a maximum of not more than 60 mph. Flight duration was to be at least 3 hours. The Scout plane, fully loaded, was to be able to climb to at least 2,000 feet in 10 minutes.

The following winter, in February, 1913, the Army issued new specifications for its Scout, and now the speed requirement was down to a range of 38–55 mph., while endurance was increased to 4 hours with a minimum range of 180 miles. Takeoff and landing, using harrowed fields or fields covered with long grass, had to be within 100 yards. Special preference was to be given airplanes equipped with an efficient stabilizing device, an engine with a self starter operable by the pilot, and an effective muffler with a cutout. Finally, the specifications required that the fuselage be protected with chrome sheet steel, .075 inch thick. The specifications, observed the *Scientific American*, "are not nearly as rigid and difficult of fulfillment as they doubtless would be if the aeronautic industry in America had kept pace with that abroad."

To meet the 1913 Army requirements for the Scout, Curtiss built his Model G, seating two, side by side. It differed considerably from his previous practice in that it used a 3-blade, geared tractor propeller, and had a fully-covered fuselage. The biplane wings had a span of 37 feet, 4 inches, with a chord of 61 inches. Interplane ailerons were still used. The wings were made as a single unit, outboard of the center section, and had a slight rearward dihedral. The unit construction of the wings and the method of fitting the tail and rudder made disassembly, for towing over the road, possible in less than 30 minutes. Landing gear was close-coupled tricycle; normally the aft fuselage remained clear of the ground, but a tail skid was fitted as protection from hard landings. Fuselage length was 24 feet, and top speed was 52 mph.

The years 1913–14 were among the busiest, and most fruitful, for Curtiss and his associates. No sooner had the Model G tractor been built than vigorous steps were taken to improve this Army type which was to become, in a later version, internationally known as the Jenny. Model J was designed—with a complete set of blueprints for the first time, plus a detailed stress analysis to satisfy Maj. Samuel Reber of the Army—but first Curtiss modified his tractor biplane ideas, experimenting with ailerons on the upper wings, a four-wheeled landing gear, and a direct-drive two-bladed propeller.

In 1914, announcement was made of the Curtiss Model J and Model J-2. The former was to satisfy requirements for the Army's Scout class, the latter its Speed Scout category. Both had two-wheeled landing gear, with a double stub skid positioned slightly forward of the wheels, and a tail skid. Both were powered by the OX engine, by now rated at 90–100 hp. The unit price for each was $7500, with floats $500 extra.

Model J was a tandem two-seater with dual controls. Its speed range was 45-75 mph., with fuel for four hours. Its initial rate of climb was 400 feet per minute, and it was designed to climb to 2,000 feet in six minutes. The upper wing of the Model J measured 40 feet 2 inches, while the lower spanned 30 feet. Chord for both was 5 feet. Turn-up ailerons 10 x 2 feet, were fitted to the upper wing only.

The single-seater Model J-2 had 24-foot wings, upper and lower, of 5-foot chord, with turn-up ailerons 7 x 2 feet fitted to both. The vertical rudder and the horizontal rudders each had a surface of 16 square feet. Speed range was 45-80 mph., while initial climbing rate was 500 feet per minute. Duration was three hours.

Busy as the Curtiss factory was in 1913–14 with scout-type projects for sale to the Army, much more was in process of development. Several new flying boats were designed and built by the winter of 1914, and in the spring, the Langley airplane was received from the Smithsonian to be put into shape for flight trials on Lake Keuka. There was also, of course, the constant pressure resulting from successive court decisions upholding the earlier judgment that the Curtiss system of aileron control infringed upon the Wright patents.

But, as if all this industry—and worry—was not enough, a major part of the Curtiss activity in this period was concentrated upon design and construction of a veritable giant of a flying boat, the "America." It was to order of Rodman Wanamaker, at a price of $25,000, and the trans-Atlantic flight it was scheduled to make was to win the $50,000 prize offered by the *London Daily Mail* for the first accomplishment of the feat.

Before discussing further the "America," a few words about two smaller flying boats built by Curtiss in 1913–14. The hulls were of the double vee-bottom, with step shape developed by Naval Constructors Richardson and William McEntee following systematic experimentation in the towing tank at the Washington Navy yard. Each was powered with an OX 90-hp. engine.

The first of these flying boats departed from usual Curtiss practice in that it was a monoplane design. Weighing almost 1200 pounds when fully loaded, its wing loading was 10 pounds per square foot. The wing was fitted with ailerons and measured 34 feet from tip to tip; it was swept back 7°. The hull, made of two layers of thin mahogany planking with heavy cotton cloth sandwiched between, was 22 feet long with a beam of 30 inches and a depth of 3 feet.

A four-passenger craft, the second of the flying boats was, essentially, a refinement over those previously offered—and widely sold. Its biplane wings had a 34-foot span and 5-foot chord, with interplane ailerons. Length of the mahogany hull was 21 feet with beam of 3 feet and depth of 3 feet. The Elliott instrument panel provided, in addition to a clock, a tachometer, air speed indicator, and barometer. Weight, empty, was listed at 1,400 pounds, and flight speed, hopefully, at "around 60 mph."

Over the years, the Curtiss organization had been growing, in technical strength as well as in other ways. Dr. Albert Zahm, who was secretary of the Langley Aerodynamical Laboratory of the Smithsonian Institution, had been engaged to head up company research, and Alfred Verville had joined the organization as an engineer.

In the design of the "America," there was additional assistance from B. Douglas Thomas, a British engineer who had worked with T. O. M. Sopwith, and Lt. J. C. Porte, invalided not long before from the British Navy by tuberculosis, who had been named pilot of the trans-Atlantic flying boat. Of at least equal value was the help in solving hydro-dynamic problems from officers of the US Navy.

As test flown June 23, 1914 from Lake Keuka, the biplane "America" had a top wing with 72-foot span, and a lower wing spanning 46 feet. Chord of each was 7 feet. Ailerons were fitted to the upper wing. Its vee-bottom, single-step hull measured 38 feet from prow to end of the vertical rudder; it had a 4-foot beam and a depth of 6½ feet. Two OX engines, mounted between the wings, powered the pusher propellers.

On the first flight, the all-up weight was less than 3,500 pounds, but for the 1,600-mile distance from Newfoundland to the Azores (the longest leg of the ocean journey as projected) it was estimated that takeoff weight would have to exceed 5,000 pounds. This, the "America" with its original hull could not manage, and numerous modifications were tried. Among these was installation of a third engine above the upper wing, driving a Garuda tractor propeller, with Olmstead-design propellers used on the other engines, further to improve performance. Several hull changes were tested before it was decided to broaden the hull beam by a sponson-type structure suggested by Richardson. Although the "America" became airborne with a weight of 6,203 pounds, late in July, the increase in fuel consumption implicit in the third engine caused it to be removed.

Outbreak of World War I in August brought cancellation of the transatlantic flight attempt. Lt. Porte returned to Great Britain to exert great influence upon the military flying boat design and construction programs of his country. Before the end of 1914, the "America" and a sister ship were delivered to the British Navy, and although tests showed them to be underpowered and to leave much to be desired in performance, 50 additional Curtiss flying boats were soon ordered. As used by the British Navy, they carried the designation, H-4.

Spectacular and substantial as was the work of Glenn Curtiss in the seven years he devoted his talents and his energies to the development and proving of the airplane, by the summer of 1914, the man and his company were but fairly started on their way. In the months and years ahead there would be other pioneering accomplishments of enduring value to aeronautics by the Curtiss organization.

Of the man, Augustus Post, early aeronaut and friend of Glenn Curtiss, once said here was "a boy who worked his way up from the making of bicycles to the making of history."

# 11/ GLENN L. MARTIN

*Down to Gehenna or up to the Throne,*
*He travels the fastest who travels alone*
RUDYARD KIPLING

The Glenn Luther Martin story, the man's life in the world of aeronautics, spans more than a half century. In it are to be found essentials of the stories of the other great American aviation pioneers . . . the dreams, the feats of daring, the quick steps forward . . . the unflagging faith that man's future was in the skies . . . the compulsion to prove that faith by action.

More than any of the early giants of the aerial age, longer even than Orville Wright, Glenn L. Martin was privileged to see improvement follow improvement until man far outraced the speed of sound. Except for a short time in the dimming, final days of his career, he savoured through the long years the rare tastes of great accomplishment and personal leadership.

Iowa-born in 1886, Martin was taken to Kansas when two and was reared in a little town with the thoroughly American name of Liberal. Before he had reached his teens, the boy was learning how to build and fly kites that far surpassed in performance those of his chums. His kites were of biplane construction, so successful that soon he was making them in the family kitchen for sale at the high price (before the turn of the century) of 25 cents.

As a youth he learned to skate on the ice of Kansas ponds. He became adept, too, at roller hockey, a sport which demands a high order of muscular and mental coordination as well as stamina. His years of cycling would be helpful when it came time to learn to fly. Another of his recreational interests, one he enjoyed all his life, was hunting. He studied the flight of his quarry and noted differences in wing structure of the ground-running prairie chickens on the one hand and of the distance-flying ducks and geese on the other. From the birds, as had Otto Lilienthal before him (*see Chapter III*), he learned much of value.

When the Martin family moved to Salina, young Glenn worked after high school and during vacations in a bicycle shop. An exciting step followed—he got a job in one of the first automobile repair shops in town. At the same time, he studied business economics at Kansas Wesleyan University and thus equipped himself with the basic knowledge of corporate and financial matters that in following years would be so valuable when he decided to establish his own airplane building companies. In 1905, the Martins moved to Southern California, to Santa Ana. Glenn went to work as an automobile mechanic, and later opened his own garage. Obtaining franchises to sell Ford and Maxwell cars, he quickly demonstrated his talents as a salesman. In later years, Martin often recalled that in 1903 he read newspaper accounts of the first flights by Wilbur and Orville Wright. He confided to his mother—Mary Minta Martin, who over the years staunchly supported and encouraged her son—that some day he, too, would fly. By 1907, perhaps before, he was devoting an increasing amount of time to aeronautics.

First, he experimented briefly with gliders; then the reports he read of flying, both in the United States and in Europe, spurred him, in 1908, to undertake construction of a powered flying machine. For his factory, Martin rented an old church in Santa Ana, left vacant when the Southern Methodists moved to new and larger quarters. For more than a year he worked, designing and building his airplane. Many evenings, his only help came from his mother, who stood holding a kerosene lamp to provide light where it was needed most. At other times, he enlisted the help of mechanics from his automobile agency.

On August 1, 1909, the airplane was ready for its first trials. They were little more than tentative hops. First, Glenn Martin had to teach himself how to fly. Courage the man had aplenty, but he was never one to take unnecessary chances. So far as he was concerned, there was nothing wrong about making haste slowly. Martin tried two successive engines in his first plane. The original engine was a Ford, taken from one of the automobiles he had for sale. It produced only 12 horsepower, and even after it had been lightened wherever possible, by substitution of hand-formed, thinsheet copper parts for cast iron, it was unsuitable if Martin were to attempt flights of any length or height. The second engine was an Eldridge, rated at 30 horsepower. Again strenuous efforts were necessary to obtain the desired reduction in engine weight.

So far as design was concerned, Martin's airplane resembled the Curtiss Gold Bug, which had been flown with such spectacular success earlier in 1909 (*see Chapter* X). The wing span of the Martin plane was 30 feet, and it measured 36 feet in length, including the bamboo outriggers and tail boom. The central structure, as well as wing spars and ribs, was made of spruce. The single-surface wings were covered with muslin. The propeller was made of laminated Oregon pine and hickory; many hours were spent in its construction to assure perfect balance. Interplane ailerons were used, but where Curtiss had affixed them to the aft struts, Martin attached them to the outer, forward struts. Landing gear was tricycle, the wheels being 20 inches in diameter.

For months, Martin went in the early mornings to his flying field just outside of town. Almost imperceptibly, the hops he made were lengthened, until one day he found himself really flying—hundreds of feet in the air. He had learned how to bank and how to turn. His airplane had become an aerial chariot, responsive to his commands.

The townsfolk were quick to urge that Glenn abandon his "wild-eyed, hallucinated, visionary" ways before he broke his neck. Pressure was applied even by fellow Presbyterians, who voiced their concern to Mrs. Martin. Now, as ever, she endorsed the work her son was doing. Glenn was all right, what he was doing was all right, she told them.

In 1910, Martin was sufficiently at home in the air to take the first step to obtain a money return on his aerial investment, which by now was more than $2,000. He announced he would give public demonstrations of his skill and would charge for admission to the flying field. When this venture proved profitable, he extended the range of his operations, and staged flight exhibitions in the Los Angeles area. The upper wing of his airplane now had an overhang of about two feet, and bent wood, wing-tip skids had been added. The forward interplane struts, at the ends of the wings, extended through the upper wing, to permit additional wire bracing. The lessons learned in the air were constantly being built into the airplane's structure.

Although, in this early period, Martin often was hard-pressed financially, he continued to expand his facilities. He moved from the old Southern Methodist church building to a vacant cannery to have more room for his aircraft construction—at one time, two airplanes were under simultaneous manufacture! More important, he employed his first engineer, Charles H. Day. A New Yorker who studied engineering at Rensselaer Polytechnic Institute, Day had practiced his profession in Alaska and California. He had worked with automobile engines, and had operated a motorcycle agency. In 1909, he built his own airplane, including the power plant. Soon after, he smashed it in an abortive flight and he then associated himself with Glenn Martin. His impressive title was chief engineer.

From then on, the Martin organization was never long without technically trained men in charge of design, although the designs were essentially according to Martin's own ideas. In 1912, Day, who was more enthusiastic about the desirability of designing a tractor-type biplane than was his employer, struck out on his own. Though the machine he subsequently built was flown, the venture was hardly a success, and Day soon returned to the Martin Company, this time to stay until 1914. In 1913–14, Charles F. Willard, an automotive engineer who previously had been an exhibition pilot for Glenn Curtiss, also worked on the design of Martin airplanes.

Perhaps more important to the growth of American aviation than the aircraft developed over the years by Glenn Martin and his associates—this is written with no disparagement to the justly famous line of Martin-built aircraft—were the graduates of the Martin "school." Day became chief engineer of Standard Aircraft Corporation in World War I. In the same period, Willard occupied a similar position with the Aeromarine Plane and Motor Corporation.

There were others: Lawrence D. Bell, who joined Martin in 1912 and soon became shop foreman . . . Donald W. Douglas, a graduate of the Massachusetts Institute of Technology, employed in 1915 . . . James H. ("Dutch") Kindelberger and James J. McDonnell, who joined the Martin organization in later years. Each would one day head his own great aircraft company. Yes, the Martin company proved to be an excellent school for those who aspired to high executive positions in aviation.

It was not until August 9, 1911, that Glenn Martin, long since an accomplished airman, got around to the formality of satisfying the requirements for a pilot's license as established by the *Federation Aeronautique Internationale* and administered in the United States by the Aero Club of America. Even so, his ACA ticket carried the low number of 56. At the same time, he was granted Expert Pilot license #2. That year, he made an extended exhibition tour that included engagements in Texas, Kansas, and Iowa, and netted more than $12,000.

In February, 1912, Martin braved the threat of license revocation to participate in an unsanctioned air meet at the Emeryville race track in Oakland, California. This was the period when the Aero Club sought, unsuccessfully, to control all air meets. His plane, self-built, was at the time described as a Curtiss type with Curtiss 80-hp. engine. Taking part in the same air show was Blanche Stuart Scott, who had soloed in September, 1910, at Hammondsport. Previously, she had flown Curtiss and Baldwin planes; now she was using one of Martin's aircraft, powered by a 60-hp. Hall-Scott engine. The same year, Martin made exhibition flights in Canada and the Midwest. In August, he made a 40-minute flight in Saskatoon, reaching an altitude of 6,400 feet.

In 1912, Martin moved his factory from Santa Ana to larger space in a downtown Los Angeles building. Soon he was constructing a float-plane, with which, on May 10, he made an over-water flight that captured the attention of the West Coast. To be sure, his exploit was almost 3 years behind Bleriot's historic Channel flight (*see Chapter* VIII) and more than a year behind McCurdy's attempt at flight across the 95 miles between Key West and Cuba—which failed within sight of the goal—but withal, it was a robust performance.

The venture consisted of a 68-mile round-trip flight between Newport Bay and Catalina Island, broken by a brief stop-over. The Los Angeles *Examiner* was especially impressed by the "scientific aspects" of the flight, noting that the barometer, aneroid, and compass "have always been his companions," as if such instrumentation provided protection equal to a wondrous amulet. The flight to Catalina required only 37 minutes; the return was more leisurely, taking 43 minutes. In beaching his hydroplane at Catalina, Martin punctured the thin hull on the rocks. The emergency patch that he applied held during the return takeoff, but failed as he landed near the shoreline of Newport Bay. Fortunately, he found it unnecessary to use his lifesaving gear, an inflated bicycle inner tube.

No sooner was he ashore than Martin emphasized to the assembled reporters the importance of his over-water flight. It was, he explained, a convincing demonstration of how an airplane could serve as a far-seeing eye for the Navy. Ranging many miles beyond the fleet, it could search out enemy vessels. No less, it could give pinpoint aim to the surface guns of the fleet.

What Martin was saying, others had said before. What he was demonstrating, others already had done. But the quietly cool authority he displayed was especially convincing, now and in all his pronouncements about the future uses of the airplane. His were the manner and action of the man who knew full well what he was saying—and doing.

Some years later, he was quoted as follows: "The way to build aircraft or do anything else worth while is to think out quietly every detail, analyze every situation that may possibly occur, and, when you have it all worked out in practical sequence in your mind, raise heaven and earth, and never stop until you have produced the thing you started to make."

The flying uniform he evolved was precisely the right combination of dash and sober utility. Black leather jacket, black leather helmet, black whipcord breeches and, of course, goggles. Such an ensemble won for him the name of "flying dude." His costume enhanced the impression that here was an aviator who, despite the daring of his exploits, must know exactly what he was doing. The glasses he wore, the high collar of his shirt, these too helped set the young man apart from—and above—others of the flying fraternity.

Early in 1912, Martin devised an aerial display that included bombing a mock fort with flour-filled bombs in the face of an horrendous defense from cannon constructed of lath and black cambric cloth. Larry Bell touched off the black powder fuses. The result was no mere extravaganza staged for the cash customers; instead, it was an awesome portent of things to come.

In 1913, Didier Masson joined the Martin organization as an instructor. A Frenchman, Masson had been a mechanic for Louis Paulhan and had learned to fly in 1910. When the Mexican revolutionary forces under General Obregon paid $5,000 for a Martin pusher biplane, powered by a 75-hp. Curtiss engine, Masson was hired as the pilot. For several months, beginning May 10, 1913, he flew for the rebels.

Masson used bombs at Guaymas Bay in operations against the beleaguered government forces led by Huerta. The bombs were little more than pieces of pipe, filled with gunpowder and plugged at both ends, but even so the dispatches reporting the action told of some loss of life and of considerable damage.

While undoubtedly the first instance where aerial bombing was employed in a warlike action in the Americas, Masson's activities do not merit being considered the first case, anywhere in the world, of bombing from an airplane.

This took place in the fall of 1911 in the Italo-Turkish war. The Italians flew Bleriots, Nieuports, Etrichs and Farmans. The principal value of the airplanes was for reconnaissance, but bombs were also dropped.

Back in the New World, as early as February, 1911, airplanes were used for military observation, on an experimental basis, along the Mexican border. Harry Harkness in an Antoinette, and Charles Hamilton in a Curtiss made the first flights; Philip Parmalee also made flights across the Mexican frontier to observe disposition of both government and rebel troops.

Few men of those early days were more ingenious than Glenn

Martin in devising ways of using the airplane. He flew motion picture personalities, with attendant mountains of publicity and high fees. Later he made as much as $700 a day when he and his plane were featured in "The Girl of Yesterday," which starred Mary Pickford. He carried cameramen who made some of the earliest aerial motion pictures.

Martin tossed a baseball to a catcher waiting below. He dropped flowers to salute a May queen. He hunted coyotes on the wing, toted copies of the Fresno (Cal.) *Republican* 24 miles to Madera, and carried a sack of mail from Dominguez to Compton. His airplane was employed, without success, in chasing two desperados.

Others might be so enthralled by aviation that they would fly for "money, or fun, or marbles; take your choice." Not so Glenn Martin. If the venture would show a dollar profit, or the equivalent in constructive press attention, then and then only would he become interested. He knew that if he was to keep his tiny factory solvent and thus insure continuing production of improved airplanes, flying for hire would be necessary, perhaps for years.

Most of his flying income was, of course, from participation in air meets and exhibitions. In 1913, he again went on the demonstration circuit, to Canada. The pusher biplane he used was powered by a 90-hp. Curtiss engine and could carry two passengers in addition to the pilot.

In 1913, too, he engaged the services of Miss Tiny Broadwick, who had been featured at country fairs as a parachutist, dropped from hot-air balloons. Martin provided Miss Broadwick with a trap seat alongside the fuselage; the parachute was so rigged that when the diminutive woman slid off her perch, a thin static line attached to the airplane opened the chute.

Though he was quick to exploit the airplane's money-making capabilities in such fashion, Martin was at least equally determined to perfect his craft for sale to the military services. In 1913, he developed what he called a military scout. Though it did not prove popular, it marked a forward step in that its design incorporated a covered fuselage with open cockpit, forward of the engine and pusher propeller. Next came the first Martin tractor, the Model T. Two versions were built, the first with a rotary engine enclosed by cowling. This model had a two-wheel landing gear plus tail skid. The second had an 8-cylinder, water-cooled engine, and four-wheel landing gear plus tail skid. In most respects, the second model was like its soon-to-appear successor, the Model TT.

In all, 17 of these Martin Model TT trainers were sold and delivered to the Army. The biplane wing span was 38 feet 8 inches, and fuselage length was 24 feet 5 inches. Gross weight was figured at 1,720 pounds. It was powered by a 90-hp. Curtiss OX-2 engine. Interplane ailerons were fitted, and the landing gear consisted of four wheels, two forward and close together, with the other two under the wing. The Army paid Martin for the airplanes, less engines. Previously, the purchase price had included engines; now the practice of providing G.F.E. (government-furnished equipment) was being initiated.

At the time the Martin airplanes were acquired, the Army's pilot training program was largely centered at North Island Field, near San Diego. The airplanes previously available had been Wright and Curtiss pushers. Describing the Martin purchase, Grover C. Loening (who had been appointed an aeronautical engineer in the Signal Corps of the Army in July, 1914) wrote in "Our Wings Grow Faster": "That something pretty drastic was needed was evidenced by the fact that when I arrived at the Army field at San Diego, eight out of a group of 14 officer pilots licensed up to that year had already been killed."

To secure replacements for the pusher airplanes he condemned as unsafe to fly, Loening recalled that "Milling [Thomas DeWitt Milling, then a lieutenant] and I rushed up to his [Glenn Martin's] plant at Los Angeles and found him most receptive to the idea of modifying and re-equipping one of his new-type tractor airplanes into a dual-control training plane. We did not actually have the money appropriated to buy it, but Martin took a chance and made very prompt delivery. And we were saved. Only a few weeks after a virtual shutdown of training, we had obtained for the army its first really safe and satisfactory training airplane, the Martin Model TT, and at the same time had started Martin on his long career of government contract work. . . . At our school our death score changed in six months. Out of twenty-nine pilots, only one was killed. . . .

And we did three or four times as much flying per pupil as had been done before."

At North Island, too, Martin worked vigorously to demonstrate the value of the airplane for bombing purposes. Lt. Riley Scott built what has been credited as the Army's first bombsight, a crude but (in the hands of a trained operator) surprisingly successful device. In the United States, there seemed to be a reluctance, in 1914, to give serious consideration to the military potential of the airplane, and little came of either the bombing experiments or the plane built with armored fuselage.

As the months passed, Glenn Martin's interests, more and more, became focused upon production of military airplanes. Nonetheless, he found time to build several airplanes for private customers. One was a tiny, short-span tractor biplane with rotary engine, for Lincoln Beachey. Another was a four-passenger tractor hydroplane, a veritable giant of the 1914 skies. Purchased by Gorat and King of Portland, Ore., the seaplane was expected to generate handsome profits, ferrying passengers across Coos Bay. Despite its advertised speed of 80 mph, and despite the enthusiastic press notices, the venture died for lack of customers, and Martin had the airplane back on his hands. Nothing daunted, he made numerous passenger-carrying flights, many of them in the Los Angeles area. Later, he took the machine to Chicago, where, in addition to carrying passengers, he won the Curtiss Marine Trophy for flying the most miles in a single day.

With Europe now at war, Martin busied himself filling military orders for both his own and foreign countries. In 1915, six Martin hydroplanes, powered by 125-hp. Hall-Scott engines, went to the Army for reconnaissance work in the Philippines. The following year, others of the same general configuration, but fitted with landing gear instead of floats, were also purchased by the Army. A score or more were bought by the Dutch government for duty in the East Indies.

The little Glenn L. Martin company, operated and owned solely by a man who stood ramrod straight and kept his own counsel, was busy indeed. So busy, in fact, that in 1916 his company looked like an attractive proposition to financiers who convinced Martin his company should be merged with the Wright organization into a $10,000,000 company to be known as the Wright-Martin Aircraft Corporation.

Not long before, Glenn Martin had predicted, "The airplane will practically decide the war in Europe. Veritable flying death will smash armies, wreck mammoth battleships and bring the world to a vivid realization of the awful possibilities of a few men and a few swift aerial demons. For the old-time war tactics are no more. The generals who realize this quickest and fight first with the flying death will win." His forecast was precisely correct, except as to time.

Finding himself a vice president with little authority or voice in the affairs of the giant corporation which swallowed his little factory, Martin was frustrated. He felt he had to do more, and quickly, to hasten the day when his predictions would come true. If it were necessary to leave the Wright-Martin organization and start again, well then, Glenn Luther Martin had the courage and the determination to do just that.

# 12/ OTHER AMERICAN PIONEERS

*Men love to wonder, and that is the seed of our science; and such is the mechanical determination of our age, and so recent are our best contrivances, that use has not dulled our joy and pride in them . . .*
*Ralph Waldo Emerson*

"When an age-long problem of such difficulty as that of the human mastery of flight is solved in a sudden and sensational manner, as by the Wright brothers last year, a stimulus is given to the art, the effect of which is seen in the immediate effort of people of an inventive and more or less mechanical turn of mind, to emulate if not surpass the achievement. Much of this endeavor, probably most of it, is doomed to failure; chiefly because the experimentalist does not realize the extreme difficulty of the problem, both from the theoretical and mechanical standpoint, and labors under the mistaken impression that a machine which is a broad imitation of the original must of itself necessarily fly."

Taken from an editorial in the *Scientific American* of June 5, 1909, this paragraph was prophetic about American reaction to the spectacular triumphs in 1908 of Wilbur and Orville Wright. In the years before World War I, literally hundreds of flying machines were constructed. Scores became airborne, if only in a faltering sort of way; a very few flew reasonably well. Most by far were pathetic failures, built by men who had neither adequate engineering knowledge to design on their own, nor mechanical competence to make good copies of airplanes that had flown.

Who were these Americans of half a century ago, these men who built their own airplanes, did their own grasscutting, and sometimes flew? They came from every walk of life; seemingly, they were alike only in that their attempts to fly were compelled by some inner driving force—"the proper parent of an art so nearly allied to invention."

What follows is, at best, only a sampling of the efforts of those early American aviation pioneers. In 1910, William E. Sommerville was mayor of Coal City, Ill. He was also the builder of an airplane and was its pilot. His airplane was of biplane design, with the upper wing measuring 45 by 5 feet, and the lower, 35 by 5 feet. The elevator was positioned 10 feet forward of the leading edge of the wings, and measured 10 by 3 feet. The tail, 8 by 5 feet, was 10 feet aft of the trailing edge. The tips of the upper wing were upturned, and to provide lateral stability, a vertical fin was also mounted on top of the wing, amidship. To further stability, the outer sections of the upper wing—just inboard of the upturned tips—were controllable venetian blinds, the slots running from leading to trailing edge.

Wrote the mayor of Coal City: "I have found the upturned ends and the central fin are sufficient to maintain lateral stability. In calm weather I had no use for the venetian blind arrangement situated near the extremities of the top plane, but with a breeze the machine rocked a little, so I opened the blind on the high side, and the machine immediately regained an even keel. I am positive, as soon as I get accustomed to being in the air, the blinds will not be required, as the upturned ends and the central fin will maintain lateral stability."

Then Mr. Sommerville related a mishap that was typical of the efforts of so many of the pioneers: "During September a few short flights were made, and October 1st a flight of 2 miles was made, and the machine flew as if on rails. The flight terminated when the engine went to pieces. The great difficulty experimenters meet with is in the securing of a reliable engine."

A year earlier, in September, 1909, Charles M. Crout had made a "short flight" of 60 feet, achieving an estimated altitude of 8 feet during his journey. This exploit at Morris Park on Long Island, N.Y., marked the first time an airplane built by a member of the Aeronautic Society of New York had gotten into the air. The

*Smithsonian Institution*

Etrich's *Taube* was a progenitor of the German class of aircraft.

*Smithsonian Institution*

Anthony H. G. Fokker designed and built this early monoplane.

Plan view of A. V. Roe's 1909 triplane.

*Smithsonian Institution*

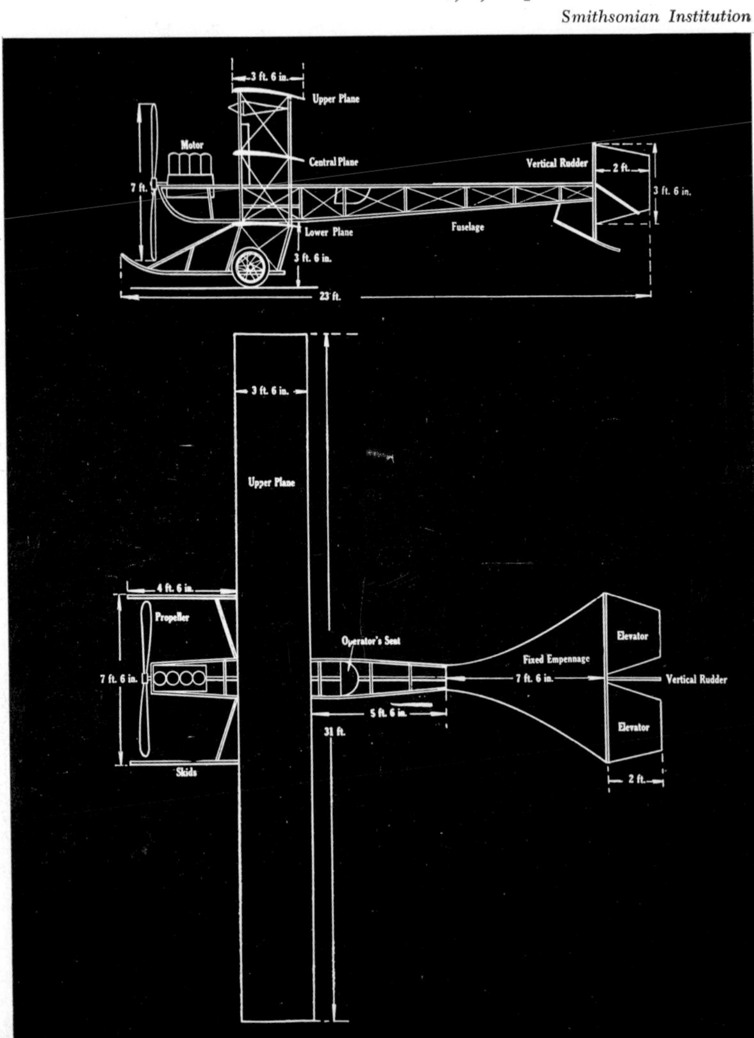

*Smithsonian Institution*

Henri Farman's biplane, 1909.

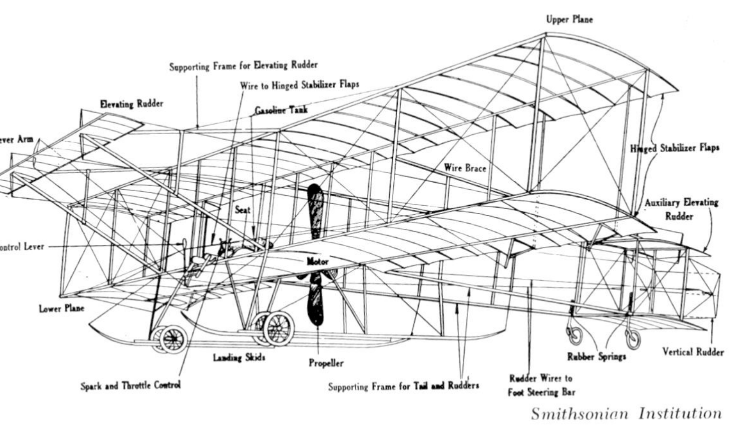


*Smithsonian Institution*

Schematic plan of Henri Farman biplane.

Voisin aircraft factory, 1908.

*Smithsonian Institution*

Smithsonian Insti

Glenn H. Curtiss won his first *Scientific American* Trophy in this airplane, the *June Bug,* on July 4, 1908.

Smithsonian Insti

Vuia "roadable airplane," 1908.

Left front view of the tetrahedral structure favored by Dr. Alexander Graham Bell.

Smithsonian Insti

*Smithsonian Institution*

Curtiss at controls of the Silver Dart, the fourth and last airplane built by the Aerial Experiment Association.

A successful carrier landing was made by Ely onto the deck of the USS *Pennsylvania* on January 18, 1911.

*Smithsonian Institution*

*Smithsonian Instituti*

To avoid the blast from the tractor propeller on his second seaplane, Curtiss reverted to pusher types on later models.

*Smithsonian Institution*

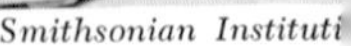

Shipboard launchi of seaplanes was test successfully on t wire rig in Septemb 1911. Navy pilot Li tenant Theodore Ellyson is at the c trols.

Construction of this flying boat won Curtiss the coveted Collier Trophy in 1912.

*Smithsonian Institu*

:onfiguration of the
ouble-vee bottom hull
f 1913–1914 Curtiss
ying boats. Mono-
lane construction was
unusual for him.

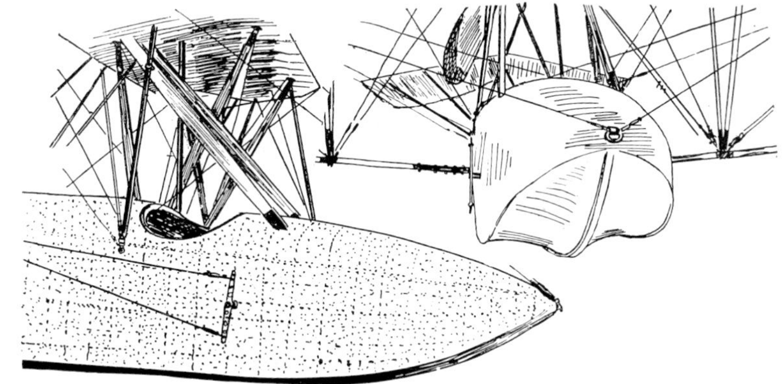

*Smithsonian Institution*

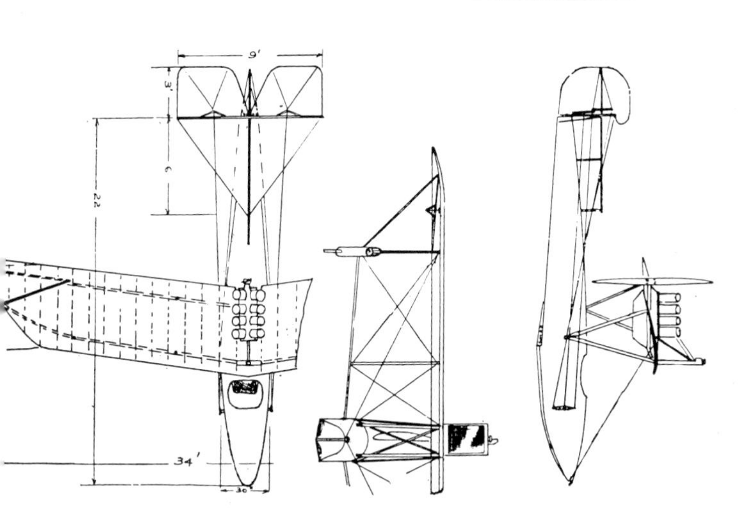


Three-view drawing of a Curtiss monoplane flying boat. Note 7-degree wing sweep.

Martin refueling his hydroplane after a flight from Catalina Island; beaching punctured the hull.

*courtesy Martin Company*

courtesy Martin Compan

Martin dropped flowers, chased gangsters, and, here, hunted coyotes.

Martin, the intrepid pilot, appeared in the movies with Mary Pickford, "America's Sweetheart."

courtesy Martin Compan

*courtesy Martin Company*

Ordered by Gorat and King, of Portland, this four-passenger seaplane, giant of 1914 skies, failed to pay its way as ferry, and came back home.

After lessons at her brother's flying school in 1910, Matilde Moisant piloted this fragile monoplane based on a Bleriot #11.

*Smithsonian Institution*

*Smithsonian Institut*

In 1912, pioneer Tom Benoist built four planes, among them this tractor biplane.

The Henrich monoplane with a student at the controls.

*Smithsonian Instituti*

Smithsonian Institution

The Boland monoplane was presented at the 1914 motorboat show.

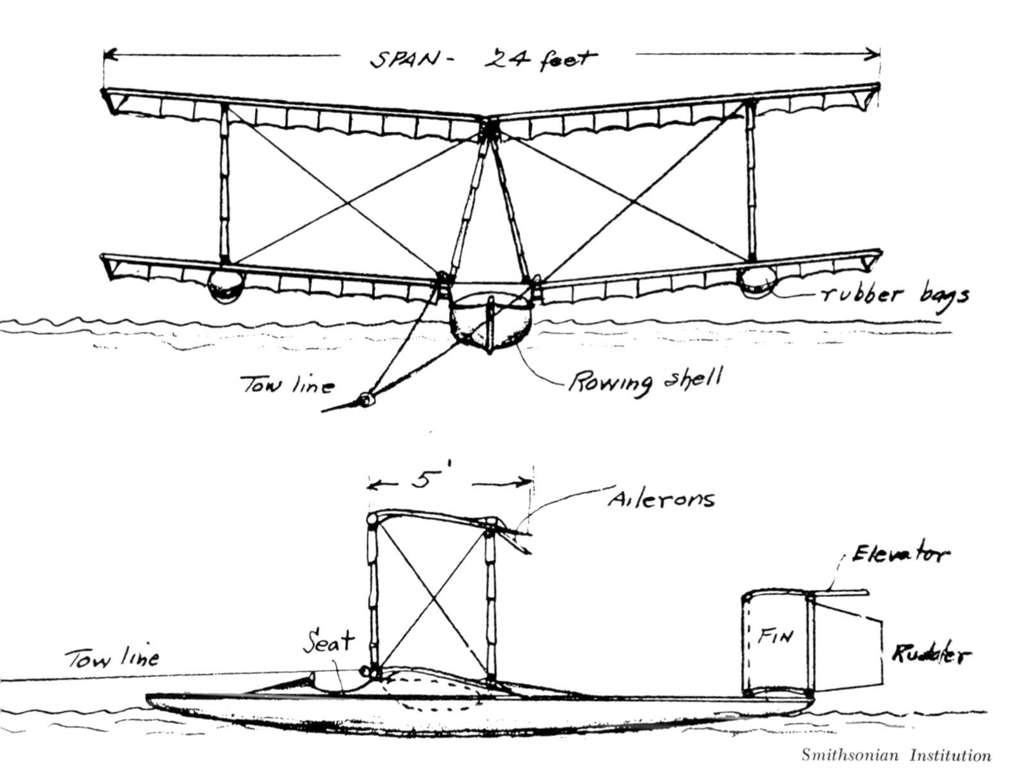


Smithsonian Institution

Grover Loening designed this glider when he was a Columbia undergraduate.

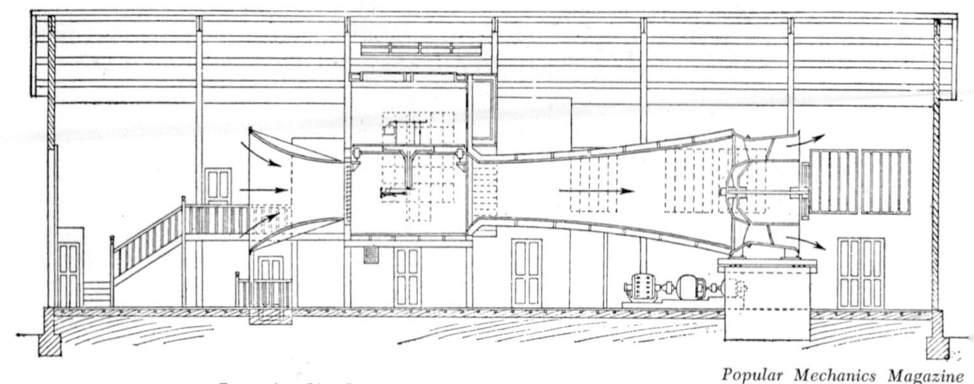

*Popular Mechanics Magazine*

Longitudinal section of Eiffel's Wind Tunnel. The course of the wind is shown by arrows. The black figure in the center chamber is the model to be tested.

The Gottingen University Aerodynamical Laboratory. The Wind Tunnel is at the left.

*Smithsonian Institution*

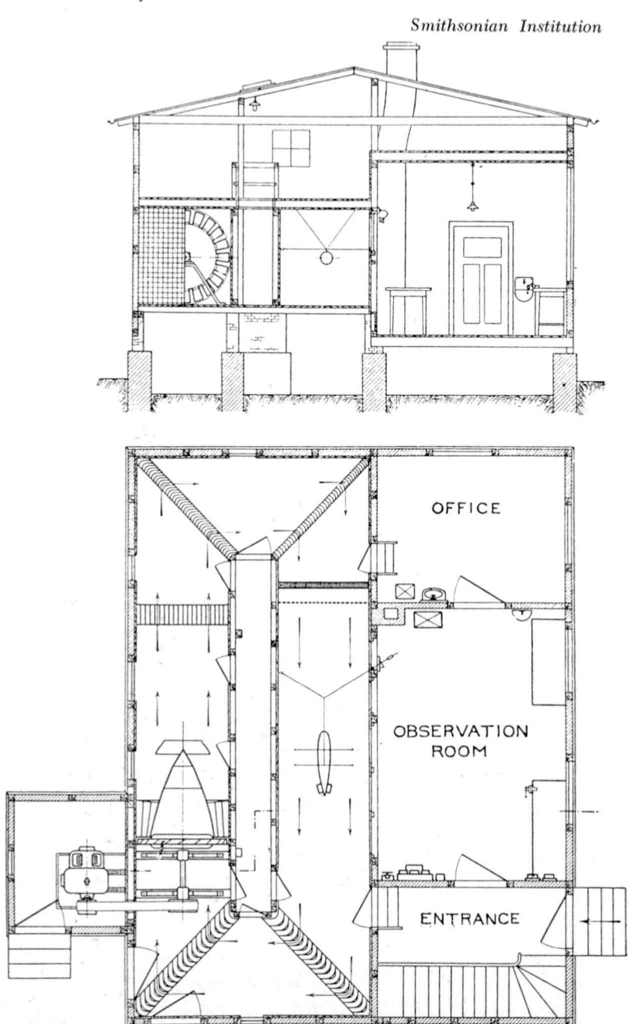

*Smithsonian Institution*

The four-cylinder, water-cooled Wright engine, circa 1909.

This seven-cylinder Hendee rotary engine was built in the United States in 1911.

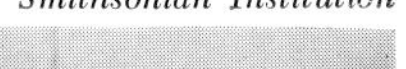
*Smithsonian Institution*

*Imperial War Museum*

B. E. 2, the first successful airplane to be produced by the Royal Aircraft Factory. It had top speed of about 70 mph,

Avro 504-K, one of the more than 17,000 in this line built during World War I.

*Smithsonian Institution*

*Saunders-Roe, Lt*

A British amphibian design which enjoye
some popularity—the Sopwith "bat-boat."

*Smithsonian Institution*

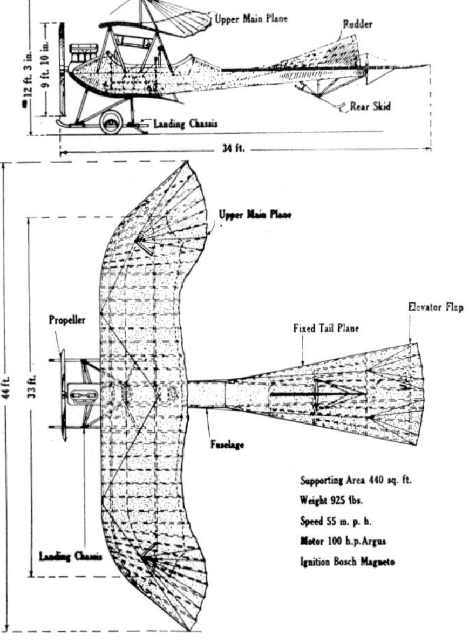


Drawings of early Albatros biplane show Etrich characteristics. Many military biplanes were produced in Germany in 1913–1914.

The second of Sikorsky's four-engine biplane
the *Ilia Mourometz*, was flown in 1914. It w
powered by Argus engines, and had a span
102 feet.

*Sikors*

builder was François Raîche, whose wife, Bessica, was one of the first two women to solo in the United States. She and Blanche Stuart Scott are credited with having flown in September, 1910. A contemporary account about the 1909 flight of the Raîche airplane said that the take-off run was at a speed of 15–18 mph, along a track into a 12–15 mph wind, and that "the balancing planes were not operative, and the airplane tipped in alighting and damaged one end of the lower plane."

Another aeronautical worker in 1909 was Morris Bokor, who built a triplane, with wings 26 by 6½ feet, forward horizontal rudder and double tail. The gap between the lower and middle wings was 5 feet, 1 foot less than that separating the middle and upper wings. The theory was that the two 8-foot-diameter pusher propellers would draw the air back, below the middle wing, thus tending to check or neutralize the interference of the lower wing. Another feature was a pendulum seat for the pilot. For power, Bokor chose a 4-cylinder A & B automobile engine, weighing 419 pounds with radiator and cooling water, which was supposed to produce 38 hp. Total airplane weight, including pilot, was 1,181 pounds. "In all probability, a larger engine will have to be installed before flight," a reporter observed.

Perhaps more determined to fly was Louis G. Erickson of Springfield, Mass., who—without technical schooling—also began construction of flying machines in 1909. In 1910, he exhibited an airplane at the Boston Aero Show. In all, he smashed four of his airplanes. Erickson's last accident was nearly fatal; hitting the top of a pine tree, he fell to earth, suffering a fractured hip and other injuries.

Many of the early aerial experimenters worked privately. Among those who worked most privately—and profitably—was Dr. William Whitney Christmas of Washington, D.C. In later years, it was testified that as early as 1890, Dr. Christmas had been studying aeronautics; that as early as 1907, he had begun construction of a biplane, and that prior to March 1, 1908, flights in it were made at Fairfax Courthouse, Virginia.

What makes the Christmas airplane of more than passing interest today is that it was controlled laterally and partially steered by interconnected ailerons, installed in the outer trailing edge of the biplane wings, substantially the same as in modern usage. A patent application was filed October 30, 1909, and a divisional patent application was filed April 22, 1910. On May 5, 1914, patent #1095548 was issued, covering the recessed ailerons. In 1918, the Christmas Airplane Company brought claim against the United States for infringing use of the patent. Sworn affidavits of Dr. Christmas and Robert H. Ions attested to straightaway flights in 1908 by the Christmas airplane equipped with ailerons. On December 18, 1923, Secretary of War John W. Weeks, acting for the United States, signed an agreement whereby the Christmas Airplane Company "sold, assigned, and conveyed to the United States the entire right, title and interest in and to the said Letters Patent #1095548. . . ." The consideration paid was $100,000.

Another of the earliest of the American pioneers who succeeded in getting into the air was Max Stupar, who was experimenting in South Chicago in 1908 with a Chanute-type glider, and soon after in a glider of his own design. Beginning in 1909–10, Stupar began building, on order, airplanes patterned after Santos-Dumont's Demoiselle (*see Chapter VIII*). He built seven and sold them at $1,000 a copy. While most of the early aeronautical workers soon turned to pursuits offering more certain financial rewards, Max Stupar made aviation his life work. Prior to World War I, he was an engineer at the Chicago Aero Works and at the Standard Aircraft Corporation. A. L. Pfitzner, an Hungarian who previously had worked with Glenn H. Curtiss on the design of aviation engines, was among the first to design and build a monoplane in the United States. It was built at Hammondsport, N.Y., and was flown in the winter of 1909–10. The wing measured 31 by 6 feet, and was unusual in that it was equipped with interconnected sliding tips, each 5 by 2½ feet. The wing tips were controlled by the steering wheel, and when one was extended fully (2½ feet), the other was completely withdrawn inside the wing. By this device, Pfitzner sought to maintain lateral stability. The single elevator, 6 by 3 feet, and a small triangular rudder were positioned 14 feet in front of the wing. The horizontal tail was 10 feet aft of the wing and measured 6 by 2 feet. The 24-hp. Curtiss engine drove a 6-foot-diameter pusher propeller, and four-wheeled landing gear was used.

In 1910, Pfitzner became assistant engineer of the aircraft company that W. Starling Burgess and Greely H. Curtis had just founded in Marblehead, Mass.—about which more directly. In its issue of July 23, 1910, the British Journal, *Flight*, published this item: "Depressed by his inability to obtain great success with his novel monoplane . . . Lt. Pfitzner is reported to have drowned himself close to Boston on the 12th inst. He had made several short flights, but was greatly disappointed because he was unable to keep going for lengthy periods."

In later years, Greely H. Curtis recalled that as a youth on a trip to Europe, he had become so interested in aeronautics that he had worked with Otto Lilienthal, father of the glider, who was killed in 1896 (*see Chapter III*). A successful hydraulic engineer, Curtis early in 1910 gave his name and support to the aircraft construction enterprise proposed by Burgess, who had become well-known as a speedboat builder.

The first product of Burgess Company and Curtis, Inc., was a biplane, mounted on twin floats and named the Flying Fish. It was powered by a 30-hp. engine, driving a pusher propeller. A. M. Herring, who had already been experimenting in aeronautics for 15 years or so and who had been associated with Octave Chanute and Glenn H. Curtiss, worked briefly with the new organization. He suggested the manner in which lateral stability was obtained without infringing the Wright system of control. Essentially, it was a modification of the Voisin principle (*see Chapter VIII*), which used fixed side panels between the wings. Herring's idea resulted in 6 (later 8) fixed triangular fins, each about 3 feet high, being mounted on top of the upper wing. The Flying Fish had outriggers fore and aft, on which were both forward and rear elevators, and a rear rudder.

The first flight of the Flying Fish was April 18, 1910. Thereafter, a number of experimental airplanes were constructed, including one of the first twin-engine airplanes, a modification of the Wright-type biplanes. This latter experiment had four propellers, two each tractor and pusher. For the most part, the Burgess Company (so it was soon officially designated) was content to use the basic designs of others. A license agreement was arranged with the Wright Company, and, for example, the Wright B, slightly modified, became the Burgess F. In 1913, the Dunne tailless design was acquired from Great Britain. By 1916, when the stock of the Burgess Company was bought by the Curtiss Aeroplane and Motor Company, the former was one of a handful of American aircraft companies which had built as many as a dozen airplanes.

Congressman Butler Ames was another of the Massachusetts men who became keenly interested in aeronautics. Early in 1909, he designed and had built an aircraft which was described as being "quite peculiar in appearance and . . . extremely simple." At a joint entertainment of the Automobile Club of America and the Aeronautic Society of New York, Representative Ames told the assembled guests about his flying machine. It consisted, he said, of a number of rectangular, low-aspect-ratio wings, placed at right angles to each other upon a longitudinal axis and separated by vertical disks. Two rods or drive shafts, set at a slight dihedral and each carrying a number of small vanes (like a paddle wheel), were turned by a 30-hp. engine. The Congressman proudly told the group that his machine had gotten off the ground, once or twice. Previously, a model of the Ames design had been shipped to the Washington Navy Yard, for testing in the towing tank.

Despite published statements in 1909 by insurance companies that "the hazard of operating or riding in aeroplanes and flying machines is NOT insurable as an accident risk," men continued to build airplanes and sought to fly them. What mattered it to the secretary of the Aeronautic Society of New York, Wilbur R. Kimball, that insurance was withheld if—as was the case—he could get the vivacious Anna Held to christen his flying machine! What, actually, did it matter that, following the ceremony, Mr. Kimball was unable to get his biplane into the air!

Flying machines were still called aeroplanes, even though the Reverend Professor Skeat, writing from Cambridge, England, in 1911, observed that *aeroplane* was a clumsy compound. What was meant, he said, was *airplane*, and the machine might just as well be called by that name. This suggestion, addressed to *Flight*, brought the polite rejoinder that "the opinion of this learned professor of

Anglo-Saxon always commands respect and attention, but we fear 'aeroplane' is too firmly established now to be ousted." In Great Britain, yes, but not for long in the United States, where Anglo-Saxon words, short and expressive, often are preferred.

The two airplanes next to be described made actual flights. Each was noteworthy because a light, small engine was the power plant. While others were seeking to use large engines, usually but little modified from heavy automobile construction, here were two experimenters, working independently, who took a different approach in their work.

M. B. Sellars of Baltimore, who also worked in Ohio and Kentucky, built his flying machine, a quadriplane, in 1908. He also constructed the air-cooled, 2-cylinder engines he used in his experiments. The wings measured 18 by 3 feet, and total weight of the airplane, including engine but less pilot, was 110 pounds. The first power plant weighed only 23 pounds and produced 4 hp. With this engine, Sellars, who himself weighed 130 pounds, was able to make short, straightaway hops. A second engine, weighing only ounces more, gave 8 hp. for short periods before overheating, and with it the Sellars airplane was able to make turns and to climb. It was clocked at 21 mph. The second of the lightweight planes, flown in 1911, was built by Donald H. Gordon of Bostinia, Calif. Instead of constructing his own engine, Gordon used a Curtiss 5-hp. twin-cylinder, air-cooled engine taken from a motorcycle. By gearing, he was able to use a 6-foot-diameter propeller, turning at 700 rpm. The weight of Gordon's little biplane was 240 pounds; the builder-pilot added 140 pounds.

Another early worker was John B. Moisant, who established a school and factory at Mineola, Long Island, in late 1909 or early 1910. For the most part, copies of European airplanes were built. Moisant's sister, Matilde, learned to fly in 1910, and continued the operation with another sister when their brother was killed December 31 of that year. The accident occurred in New Orleans, where he had taken a troupe of international pilots for exhibition flights. Giuseppe Bellanca, newly arrived from Italy, worked at the Moisant school as a general handy man in 1912–13, when five young officers from Mexico were given flight training. In 1913, too, the Moisant factory built a number of airplanes, among them one powered by a 50-hp. Gnome-rotary engine, which Frank Kantner had designed. Three Morane-Saulnier monoplanes were built in 1914. Powered by 80-hp. Gnome rotary engines, they were for the revolutionary forces of Carranza and Villa in Mexico. The planes were under the command of Capt. Alberto Salinas Carranza, who learned to fly at the Moisant school and has been called the founder of Mexican aviation.

In February, 1912, President William Howard Taft attended the annual banquet of the Aero Club of America. "I believe in the future of aviation," he said, "and I think that any encouragement or quasi-official recognition that my presence here may give is quite in order."

With government support so limited, it should have been easy to see the reasons underlying the situation which the President went on to describe: "We are in friendly rivalry with France in many things, and it is perhaps not pleasing to note that she is outstripping us in the number of her aviators." He might have included the other major European nations in his comments, because they, too, were forging ahead of the United States in aviation.

Despite the lack of positive support given them, American pioneers continued to design and to build airplanes. Tom Benoist was another of these. He built and flew his first biplane in 1910 in St. Louis. His early designs were not unlike those of Glenn Curtiss, and as Curtiss had done, Benoist became interested in water-based aircraft. In 1912, Benoist built a pusher biplane, a tractor biplane, a float plane, and then a flying boat. Also in 1912, Tony Jannus attracted favorable attention for the Benoist flying boat by piloting it 1,970 miles from Omaha to New Orleans in 39 days.

Early in 1914, the first regularly scheduled airline service in the United States was started in Florida, using two Benoist flying boats powered by 75-hp. Roberts engines. The route flown was 19 miles, across Tampa Bay, between St. Petersburg and Tampa. In 1914, also, a two-engine flying boat was built by Benoist for a transatlantic flight, but the war put an end to such attempts. Benoist was killed in 1917, on the ground as luck would have it—in a streetcar accident.

Albert S. Henrich and his brother, Arthur, were florists in Baldwin, Long Island. They also were interested in aviation, and in 1911 they built a monoplane powered by a 3-cylinder Anzani air-cooled engine. Its wing spanned 28 feet and had rounded tips. Weight was 350 pounds, with engine, and lateral control was by wing-warping. Matched against a French Deperdussin that had been enjoying a reputation for speed on Long Island, the Henrich monoplane was the winner. For several years, the brothers continued to design and build airplanes.

Still another of the American pioneers was Frank E. Boland, whose aerial experimenting began in 1907. By 1908 he had acquired a machine which later was described as almost unflyable. Early in his work, Boland sought ways of obtaining control that would not infringe the Wright patents. The solution he chose incorporated hinged, vertical triangular flaps or jibs that were used for both steering and lateral stability. Boland's flying machine had no tail or vertical rudder, although he made use of a horizontal rudder, mounted forward. In 1911–12, he built a biplane with this type of control. It weighed about 800 pounds, had an 8-cylinder engine of his own design, and was flown with enough success to encourage Boland to build a flying boat of similar design. In it, Frank Boland was killed at Port of Spain, in 1913. Boland's small manufacturing organization was a nucleus of the Aeromarine Plane and Motor Corporation, formed in 1914.

In 1911, Walter L. Fairchild built a tractor monoplane, which he flew from Mineola, Long Island. It was of special interest because he used steel tubing for construction. Fairchild also built a larger airplane, powered by a 100-hp. Emerson engine, driving two propellers which revolved in opposite directions. In general line, the Fairchild designs resembled the French Antoinette.

Edson F. Gallaudet, reported to have experimented with kites as early as 1898, organized an engineering company in 1910, which built airplanes in Connecticut and Rhode Island until after World War I. The predecessor organization of Consolidated and the Convair Division of General Dynamics, Gallaudet Engineering Company was best known, prior to World War I, for the "Bullet," a monoplane of radical design.

The pusher propeller of the Bullet was located at the tail and was driven through a shaft by an enclosed engine in the nose. The wings measured 14 feet, with chord tapering from 8 feet at the fuselage to 6 feet at the tip. A tubular steel spar, running from wing tip to wing tip through the fuselage, made possible changing the angle of incidence in flight. Although the flights made by the Bullet showed its performance potential to be great, the design included so many innovations it was perhaps inevitable that the degree of reliability demonstrated left much to be desired.

Grover Cleveland Loening, an undergraduate at Columbia University, saw his first flying machine in the fall of 1908, at Morris Park on Long Island. Even the fact that the craft refused to become airborne failed to dampen the young man's enthusiasm. More than a half century later, with a distinguished career behind him, Loening was continuing to display the same enthusiasm for aeronautics. For Loening, it was a quick and easy task to organize the Columbia University Aero Club. The following spring, the next step, design and construction of a flying boat glider, was taken. The expectation, of course, was that as soon as flight experiments had been made towing the glider by motorboat, an engine would be installed, and real flight begun.

"The assurance with which the plans were drawn, however, did not cover one single bit of knowledge of hydro-planing technique, of suction on hulls, of step construction, and of what later was to prove one of the great hurdles of all water-flying machines—the ability to get up on the step, hydro-planing, and then with constantly diminishing resistance and suction of the water to become gradually airborne." Loening's wry remembrance, in later years, of the blissful ignorance which accompanied this first effort to fly is concluded by his comment that the faster the glider was towed, the more deeply the hull—a canvas racing shell—dug into the water.

In 1909, Loening studied for his master's degree, and was permitted to concentrate upon aviation and aerodynamics. His M.A., awarded in June, 1910, was the first of its kind in the United States. In his search for truth, he corresponded with the Wright brothers and Alexander Graham Bell, from whom he received considerable help and encouragement.

In 1911, he went to work as an engineer for Willis McCornick, whose Queen Aeroplane Company for the most part built copies of Bleriot monoplanes. The following year, Loening mounted a Bleriot fuselage and wings on a wooden float, and made a few short hops. In 1913, an improved version, its frame and floats of metal, was designed and built. The first flight showed that the wing-warping mechanism needed adjustment. Before the "Aeroboat" could be taken out of the water, a sudden afternoon thunderstorm battered the craft beyond all hope of repair.

Disappointed by the smashup of his flying boat, Loening was far from discouraged. He went to Dayton for a year to work with Orville Wright (Wilbur had died in 1912). After this, he was an aeronautical engineer for the War Department until July, 1915, when he became vice president and general manager of the newly organized Sturtevant Aeroplane Company.

Except for the limited needs of the exhibition circuit, there was no real market for airplanes in the United States before World War I. To be sure, wealthy sportsmen bought flying machines, but only a very few. There was no commercial aviation business, and military orders could be counted in ones and twos.

In those early years, despite this lack of promise of financial reward, Americans continued their aeronautical pioneering. They wanted to fly; so they did!

# 13/ THE RESEARCH LABORATORIES

*The simplest of our flying machines is aerodynamically exceedingly complex. We have always been prepared to design and build aircraft to meet extraordinarily severe conditions. There is only one yardstick by which we can expect to be judged—results. We need all our skill —and skill is art, though not the whole of it.*

SIR WILLIAM S. FARREN

The 14th annual report of the Aeronautical Society of Great Britain, for the year 1879, contained the harsh, though true, judgment that: "Mathematics up to the present day have been quite useless to us in regard to flying." How different the situation has been in the past 50 years, when the science of fluid mechanics has been employed so fruitfully by mathematicians and physicists to unlock secrets of nature that could be used in explaining not only *why* it was possible for man to fly, but also *how* he could fly more successfully.

To be sure, for centuries prior to the first flights by Wilbur and Orville Wright in 1903, men of mathematics had built, piece by patient piece, a body of knowledge that one day would be of great value in the establishment of a new science—aerodynamics. There was Leonardo da Vinci, who in the 15th Century wrote that "the movement of the air against a fixed thing is as great as the movement of the movable thing against the air which is at rest." There was Sir Isaac Newton, who, two hundred years later, published the monumental "Philosophia Naturalis Principia Mathematica" in which he stated the first theory of air resistance as deduced from the principles of mechanics and, perhaps equally important, pointed out that the same law applied equally to water and air. There were many others . . . d'Alembert, Helmholtz, Bernouilli, Euler, Kirchhoff, Rayleigh . . .

Not all of the early statements of the principles of fluid mechanics were correct. In fact, the falseness of Newton's statement of proportionality between the force acting on a surface element and the square of the sine of its angle of inclination has been blamed by some critics for having been a delaying influence on the development of mechanical flight. More likely, the influence of Newton and other mathematicians on the efforts of the early aeronautical pioneers was negligible; they seldom had faith in theories.

Beginning in the 19th century, the principles of fluid mechanics were rigorously appraised by engineers and physicists. Bodies in motion were studied, both in the air and in water, by use of a "whirling-arm" device (in the United States, for example, by Langley in 1886). A little later, the resistance of bodies moving through water was determined in towing tanks. The findings from such research tools were of interest to shipbuilders and munitions makers who had pressing need for means to improve the products of their yards and ordnance works.

Newton in the 17th century had studied spheres which he dropped from the dome of St. Paul's Cathedral in London. Two hundred years later, Gustave Eiffel made similar experiments in Paris, from a platform high up on the tower which bore his name. In England, beginning in the 1870's, Herbert Wenham and Horatio Phillips devised successful wind tunnels, the most useful of the tools employed in aerodynamic research. As early as 1891, Nikolai E. Joukowski built a wind tunnel with a 2-foot-diameter test section at the University of Moscow. By the beginning of the 20th century, wind tunnels were being used also in the United States by the Wright brothers and Albert F. Zahm, and in France and in Germany.

Such was the state of affairs in 1903 when the Wright brothers took to the air. Disillusioned by the inaccuracies they found in data such as Lilienthal had compiled from his glider experiments in Germany (*see Chapter III*), they relied almost entirely upon the results of their own wind tunnel investigations. These they verified as best they could by measurement during flights of their gliders.

Wilbur and Orville Wright continued, after 1903, to be self-sufficient. They had been the first to attain sustained flight in a machine heavier than air, and now, they concentrated upon two tasks: (1) The merchandising of their invention, and (2) the defense of what they believed to have been a development solely theirs. The latter effort, intensified by Orville after Wilbur died in 1912, may well have slowed the progress of aeronautics in the United States. Especially with respect to alleged infringement by Glenn Curtiss against the Wright patents, the litigation was long and often acrimonious. Elsewhere, the Wright patents had little retarding effect upon the vigorous forward push of aeronautics which began about 1906.

Meanwhile, in Europe, the mathematicians were making real progress in developing theories that would explain, for example, the lift obtained by means of a curved wing at zero angle of attack. Frederick W. Lanchester, British engineer and automobile manufacturer, began his experiments and studies in 1894. In 1897, he read a paper to the London Physical Society which disclosed a remarkably sophisticated understanding of the physical concepts of modern wing theory. In 1907 and 1908, he published two volumes of his well-developed ideas. The importance of Lanchester's work was first recognized by the Germans, not the English.

A logical explanation was given, in 1927, by Ludwig Prandtl: ". . . As a matter of fact we in Germany were better able to understand Lanchester's book when it appeared than you in England. English scientific men, indeed, have been reproached for the fact they paid no attention to the theories expounded by their own countryman, whereas the Germans studied them closely and derived considerable benefit therefrom. The truth of the matter, however, is that Lanchester's treatment is difficult to follow, since it makes a very great demand on the reader's intuitive perceptions, and only because we had been working on similar lines were we able to grasp Lanchester's meaning at once. At the same time, however, I wish to be distinctly understood that in many particular respects Lanchester worked on different lines than we did, lines which were new to us, and that we were able to draw many useful ideas . . ."

Two others also had developed independently, and as early as 1903, the mathematical foundation of the theory of lift. They were

M. Wilhelm Kutta, who became interested in aerodynamic theory as a result of Lilienthal's gliding experiments, and Nikolai E. Joukowski, who had pioneered in aeronautical research in Russia.

Even before Wilbur Wright went to France in 1908, to make the first public demonstrations of the Wright Flyer—thus to dispel beyond all doubt the success of the airplane—systematic investigation of aeronautical problems had been undertaken at a number of European educational institutions and laboratory centers established specifically for the purpose. What was happening, first in France, Germany and Russia, and then in England and in Italy, was in sharp contrast to the lack of interest shown in aeronautical research in the United States. Here, with the closing of Langley's laboratory at the end of 1903, further improvement of the airplane was left almost entirely to the cut-and-try efforts of the builders themselves.

Two examples of the vigor of European aeronautical research in this early period will suffice. In 1905, Gustave Eiffel built a laboratory at the foot of the Eiffel Tower to continue his aviation work begun the previous decade. Here, over a period of seven years, more than 4,000 experiments and tests were conducted. The wind tunnel he used had a test section of about 5-foot diameter, with an air speed of 40 mph. In 1912, Eiffel, then 80, completed a new and larger laboratory at Auteuil. It included a wind tunnel of 6.5-foot-diameter test section, capable of a maximum speed of about 70 mph. Eiffel was especially interested in "scale effect," and worked intensively to develop an accurate "coefficient of enlargement" that would enable him to convert data obtained from experiments with small models to full-scale values. His "The resistance of the air and aviation experiments conducted at the Champ-de-Mars Laboratory" was considered an aeronautical classic when it was published in 1910. It became available in the United States and Great Britain in 1913, when J. C. Hunsaker, at the time a young Naval officer, translated the work into English.

It should be noted that in this period there were two other aeronautical laboratories in France: The Institut Aerotechnique de St. Cyr, founded by Henry Deutsch de la Meurthe and presented to the University of Paris, and the research facilities of the Army at

Chalais-Meudon. It might be noted, too, that a chair of aeronautics was established at the University of Paris, reportedly at a cost of $100,000, the gift of Basil Zaharoff, the munitions maker.

In Germany, in 1908, an aeronautical laboratory was established at Göttingen University, with Ludwig Prandtl in charge. For nearly half a century this man, who has been credited more than any other with having given modern theory its practical mathematical form, continued to make valuable contributions. Prandtl is perhaps best known for his work in the field of what he called "Grenzschicht," known as the "boundary layer" in English. Of importance equal to his personal work in aerodynamics was Prandtl's ability to teach, and to inspire, talented students to extend the researches he had begun.

Prandtl's laboratory, in the early days, was a simple affair, located some distance from the university proper. His principal research tool was a closed-circuit wind tunnel with a test section 6.5 feet square. Although it had only low speed (about 25 mph), the pains which had been taken to insure smooth air flow made possible important aerodynamic investigations.

As was the case in France, in Germany there were several other aeronautical laboratories, including facilities at technical schools at Aachen and Berlin, test equipment of the Deutsche Versuchsanstalt für Luftfahrt at Adlershof, and the experimental facilities of the larger aircraft manufacturers, notably the Zeppelin Airship Company. Great Britain and Italy were slower than the other major European nations to establish aeronautical research on a rational basis. It was not until 1909 that the British Advisory Committee for Aeronautics was formed to coordinate and expand theoretical and experimental work in aeronautics. Once started, however, the British made rapid strides. About the same time, aeronautical experimentation in Italy was made the responsibility of the Italian Specialist Brigade of Engineers.

In the United States, as late as 1911, none of the universities had yet established formal courses for the systematic study of aerodynamics. Nowhere in America was there an aeronautical research laboratory. In 1912, a compilation in the annual report of the Secretary of the Navy showed the United States to be lagging far behind the other world powers in expenditures for aviation. The sums appear tiny today, but in days when a nickel would still buy a smokable cigar, they were substantial. France spent $7,400,000; Russia, $5,000,000; Germany, $2,250,000; Great Britain and Italy, $2,100,000 each; Japan, $600,000, and the United States, $140,000.

In retrospect, American reluctance prior to World War I to appropriate funds for aeronautical development is understandable. The airplane offered little promise of early utility for commercial purposes, and in the United States there was little of the impetus felt so keenly in Europe to construct an air armada for military use.

Though the reasons for America's lack of adequate support of aeronautical effort—in terms of research, procurement and service use—may have been rational, they were of little comfort to the small group of men who felt it was a disgrace that the nation which had been the birthplace of the airplane should have fallen so far behind in the aeronautical race. By 1910, these men were calling repeatedly for action—for establishment of a research center, for purchase of more airplanes by the military services.

Among these were Albert F. Zahm, who had worked with Langley, and Capt. Washington Irving Chambers, in charge of Naval aviation. They spoke plainly; they spoke often. On September 21, 1912, in a review of aviation which was later incorporated in the annual report of the Secretary of the Navy, Capt. Chambers said:

"Little more than a year ago our knowledge of the effect of air currents upon airplane surfaces was almost entirely a matter of theory. The exact information available was so meager that airplanes were built either as copies, slightly modified, of other machines, or else by way of haphazard experiment. This state of affairs obtains to some extent in the United States today, although in Europe airplane construction is now largely based on scientific data obtained at notable aerodynamic laboratories.

"The intuitive, hasty, and crude methods of the pioneer can not succeed in competition with the accurate and systematic methods of the scientific engineer, and it is beginning to dawn upon our perceptions that through lack of preparation for the work of the scientific engineer, i.e., through delay in establishing an aerodynamic laboratory, a waste of time and money, a decline of prestige, and an unnecessary sacrifice of human life has already resulted."

As early as 1911, a plan had been worked out for establishment of an aeronautical laboratory, to be supervised by the Smithsonian Institution and operated by the National Bureau of Standards. The Navy's Bureau of Construction and Repair protested the plan on the ground the new laboratory would largely duplicate the work of its model basin (in fact, important work on seaplane float design was being done there). The Navy's Bureau of Steam Engineering felt its experimental station at Annapolis was suitable for the testing of airplane engines and propellers. The War Department favored separate, though non-duplicating, research effort by the War and Navy Departments. With such opposition voiced, the plan was stillborn.

Two men who were most influential in the drive for a national aeronautical laboratory were Dr. Alexander Graham Bell and Dr. Charles Doolittle Walcott. Bell, a regent of the Smithsonian, had been a supporter of Langley; in his own right he had performed interesting research with tetrahedral kites and had been instrumental in formation of the Aerial Experiment Association (*see Chapter IX*). Walcott had succeeded Langley as secretary of the Smithsonian, and was determined that the institution should resume its position as a leader of aeronautical science in the United States. There were others, and as the years passed their number grew.

Late in 1912, President William Howard Taft created a 19-man commission, headed by Dr. R. S. Woodward, president of the Carnegie Institution, to study the problem. Unfortunately, Taft appointed the commission without the "advice and consent of the Senate." Authorizing legislation, introduced in the Congress in 1913, to implement the commission's recommendation—for prompt establishment of an aeronautical research laboratory in the Washington area, to be directed by the regents of the Smithsonian—was not to be granted. Even the prior expenses of the commission, totaling $581.66, went unappropriated.

Meantime, starts were made by technical schools in the study of aeronautic problems. In 1911, Worcester Polytechnic Institute constructed a whirling table for use by Prof. David L. Gallup. It was built in a shallow pond, thus enabling investigation of both aerodynamic and hydrodynamic matters, and was used principally in the study of propeller design. In 1913, the Massachusetts Institute of Technology decided to begin courses in aerodynamics, and requested the Navy to designate a qualified officer to prepare and conduct them. J. C. Hunsaker, who had worked with Eiffel, was named, and soon undertook construction of a wind tunnel at the school. The University of Michigan also offered courses in aeronautical engineering in this period.

In 1913, the Smithsonian regents decided to reopen Langley's old laboratory. An Advisory Committee for the Laboratory was appointed with representatives of the War, Navy, Agriculture and Commerce Departments serving as members. Although President Woodrow Wilson approved service on the committee by the government representatives, the Comptroller of the Treasury soon ruled that such service—even though unpaid—was unlawful without the authority of Congress, and the Smithsonian's effort was severely crippled. After several meetings of the committee, the Langley Laboratory was again closed.

World War I broke out in August, 1914. Later that year, the Smithsonian again studied "the need for a National Advisory Committee for Aeronautics." Its findings were contained in a memorial addressed to the Congress February 1, 1915. Pertinent sentences from the document read: "This country led in the early development of heavier-than-air machines. Today it is far behind. When the European war broke out, France had about 1,400 airplanes, Germany 1,000, Russia 800, Great Britain 400, the United States 23 . . . a National Advisory Committee for Aeronautics cannot fail to be of inestimable service in the development of the art of aviation in America. Such a committee, to be effective, should be permanent and attract to its membership the most highly trained men in the art of aviation and such technical services as are connected with it. Through the agency of sub-committees the main advisory committee could avail itself of the advice and suggestions of a large number of technical and practical men. . . . The aeronautical committee should advise in relation to the work of the Government in aeronautics and the coordination of the activities of governmental and private laboratories, in which questions concerned with the study of the problems of aeronautics can be experimentally investigated."

The Navy heartily endorsed the idea in a letter signed by Franklin D. Roosevelt as Acting Secretary, but by the time a Joint Resolution authorizing creation of such a committee had been prepared, the Congress was pressing toward the closing of its session in early March. This shortness of time—rather than the reported opposition by President Wilson to establishment of such an aeronautical research agency at a time when the United States was seeking so diligently to maintain strict neutrality in the war—doubtless explains why Rep. Ernest W. Roberts (himself a Smithsonian regent, and also a member of the House Committee on Naval Affairs) attached the resolution as a rider to the Naval Appropriations Act.

So it was that, on March 3, 1915, organization of America's aeronautical research establishment, the National Advisory Committee for Aeronautics, was approved. The part played by the NACA in the successful effort by the United States over the years was large indeed. In 1958, the NACA became the nucleus of the National Aeronautics and Space Administration.

In a dozen short years, following the first flights of Wilbur and Orville Wright, a very great change in aviation took place. The designer learned to look to the mathematician and the physicist for vital assistance in solving problems that seemed to multiply with progress. This learning process was slow; it is ironic that in the United States, in those early days, it was slowest of all countries.

# 14/ THE HEART OF THE AIRPLANE

*Give me the engine, and I'll*
*fly a barn door.*

ANON.

They called them explosion engines in the earliest days. And so, in a sense, they are, machines in which energy is translated directly into mechanical power by causing a fast rate of burning behind a piston within a cylinder. Wilbur and Orville Wright used such an engine for their first flights, and for the next 36 years (until the advent of the turbojet engine in 1939) all powered, heavier-than-air flight depended upon man's development of this prime mover—the internal combustion engine.

As early as 1680, Christian Huygens, the remarkable Dutch mathematician and physicist, worked out the practical details of an internal combustion engine—to be fueled by gunpowder. A century later, Street proposed an engine driven by a flame-ignited explosive mixture of vaporized turpentine and air, and in 1838 Barnett provided the vital improvement of compressing the explosive charge prior to ignition. Despite Sir George Cayley's suggestion in 1810 that such engines be harnessed to propel aircraft (*see Chapter II*), nearly a century of further development was required before the internal combustion engine was transformed from a ponderous machine—turning over at little more than 200 rpm., and weighing a thousand pounds or more for each horsepower of work performed—into a power plant sufficiently light and reliable to make possible powered, heavier-than-air flight.

It was not until the 1860's when Lenoir built his first useful, though crude, gas-fueled internal combustion engines that this type of power plant really began to mature. In 1862, Beau de Rochas stated explicitly the principle of the four-stroke cycle:—1, Drawing the fuel and air into the cylinder by suction during the first down stroke of the piston; 2, compressing the gaseous fuel mixture during the first up stroke; 3, ignition of the compressed charge and expanding the exploded gases during the second down stroke, and 4, discharge of the burned gases during the second up stroke. Fourteen years later, Otto built his first de Rochas 4-cycle engine. It and others Otto built were so successful that in later years this became the most common type among the internal combustion engines and often was known as the Otto cycle.

Among the first to work determinedly and effectively at the task of reducing the weight of the internal combustion engine and of increasing the power output by speeding up its operations were the Germans, Gottlieb Daimler and Karl Benz. In 1886, Daimler built a gasoline-fueled engine that, at least by the standards of his day, was both light and fast—it weighed 88 pounds-per-horsepower and ran at 800 rpm. His first tricycle—a three-wheeled road-runner that preceded the four-wheeled automobile and the two-wheeled motorcycle—was built in 1886, and his first automobile in the following year.

Benz also constructed small engines for tricycle use about the same time. In 1889, the only automobile displayed at the Paris exhibition was powered by a Benz motor. In 1889, Daimler made arrangements with Panhard and Levassor for manufacture of his engines in France, and rapid development of the motor car in that country may be said to have been fairly started as a result.

Another of the pioneering engine manufacturers was the de Dion-Bouton firm, which used a high tension magneto ignition system on high-speed engines (1500–1800 rpm.) that produced large powers. The original de Dion-Bouton engines were air-cooled, with finned cylinders, and had aluminum crankcases.

The first internal combustion engine used for aerial application was of the Lenoir type. It was built in 1872 to power Paul Haenlein's airship in Germany. A 4-cylinder, five horsepower engine, it ran at only 40 rpm., and consumed about 250 cubic feet per hour of gas taken from the balloon itself. In 1897, Daimler engines were installed in the unsuccessful airships built by Schwarz, and by Baumgarten and Wolfert. There was insufficient interest in airship construction in the years just before and after the turn of the century to warrant the heavy expense of developing a really light-weight engine. Nor was the growing motor car industry enough concerned with weight reduction to produce the kind of power plant the would-be aviators needed.

When Prof. Samuel P. Langley (*see Chapter IV*) began searching in 1900 for someone in Europe to build a lightweight engine for his airplane he did so only after an American manufacturer had failed in a year-long effort to construct a 12-hp. engine not more than 100 lb. in weight. Charles Manly, Langley's assistant, canvassed French motor makers without success. Albert de Dion told him that the engine he wanted was quite out of the question. If anyone could build it, he, de Dion, could. Since he could not, it was obviously an impossible project! And yet, with the urge to fly so compelling on both sides of the Atlantic, something had to be done about providing suitable engines. First came Manly's remarkable radial engine, then the Wright brothers built their light, simple adaptation of the automobile engine, and finally, brilliant engineers, especially in Europe, produced a whole family of internal combustion engines, some of them excellent producers of power, for aircraft propulsion.

Between 1900 and the beginning of World War I, most of the basic design possibilities for aircraft use of the internal combustion engine were investigated, at least to the extent of experimental construction. There were vertical types and vee-types, radials and rotaries, and horizontally opposed engines. Both carburetion, in many variants, and direct fuel injection were used. Yes, those were years of vigorous, fruitful aircraft engine development. If many of the earliest designs failed for lack of suitable structural materials and manufacturing techniques, the experience of the engine makers was no different from that in many fields of endeavor—including that involving the design and construction of airframes. Charles Matthews Manly, the Cornell University-trained engineer, has been called the outstanding genius of early aviation powerplant design. Certainly, the task he undertook was enormously difficult. When he started, he had very little to work with. There may have been the germ of the idea for a rotary engine in the unsuccessful efforts of S. M. Balzer of New York to build an engine for Langley, but it remained for Manly to solve the seemingly endless problems of design and construction.

Manly's engine was a 4-cycle, 5-cylinder radial with a bore of 5 in. and a stroke of 5½ in. The cylinders were ⅙ in. thick, made from steel spun from a flat plate. Into them was shrunk a cast-iron liner of the same thickness. The form of construction was novel; Washington machine shops said flatly it was impossible to do the job, so Manly had to show them how. The five cylinders were mounted on a steel, barrel-shaped crank case. The pistons were of cast iron, of lighter weight and more sophisticated design than would become general for years ahead. Everything had to be made specially—the ignition system, the carburetor, even the spark plugs.

How well Manly succeeded in this project may be seen in its weight; dry, it was only 125 lb., and with all accessories and cooling water, only 207.5 lb. During three runs, nonstop for 10 hours each time, it produced a constant 52.4 hp. at 950 rpm. This engine, the first of the "modern" aircraft powerplants—a type which after World War I was to be widely used—is now on permanent display at the Smithsonian Institution.

The way Wilbur and Orville Wright solved their power-plant problem was much different. The fact that they were satisfied to build what was essentially a lightened adaptation of the conventional 4-cylinder automobile engine of their day is not to be considered a reflection upon their abilities. Quite properly, they felt that solution of the aerodynamic and control problems of the airplane was of paramount importance, and that all they needed in an engine was sufficient power and yet light weight and strength, to get them into the air. Their first engine weighed more than four times as much, per horsepower, as Manly's. How right they were in their reasoning was demonstrated December 17, 1903. Although their water-cooled engine, with its 4-in. bore and stroke, generally followed automobile practice, the Wrights did not hesitate to make the major design modifications they felt necessary. For example, they positioned the four cylinders horizontally, with the automatic inlet valve located over the exhaust valve. Fuel was fed by gravity to a tube leading through the water jacket where it was vaporized, and then into the inlet manifold where it was mixed with the incoming air. The cylinders and pistons were made of cast iron, the crankshaft machine steel, and the crankcase and water jacket cast aluminum alloy.

The Wrights' first engine weighed about 200 lb., including all accessories and cooling water, and produced 12 hp. at 1,090 rpm. By 1906, they had overcome earlier heating troubles. Other improvements included better machining of the cylinders and pistons, and the addition of a fuel pump. Now they could hold power output at 25 hp. at 1,300 rpm. (the 1903 engine output dropped by almost 25 per cent after running a few minutes).

Not long after, the Wright brothers began building engines producing up to 40 hp. Their four cylinders were now vertical on an aluminum crankcase. Fuel was fed by injection into the inlet port of each cylinder. Beginning 1912–13, they built a 6-cylinder vertical engine rated at 60 hp.; both fuel injection and carburetion were available. Wilbur and Orville Wright constructed about 100 4-cylinder and about 50 6-cylinder power plants. Generally conventional, their engines showed consistent improvement over the years, and reflected the philosophy of the brothers that reliability rather than lightness was what was most important. A 1910 compilation of aviation engines showed about 76 types being constructed in Europe and the United States. Of these, 22 were 4-cylinder verticals and two were 6-cylinder verticals. The 4-cylinder engines of that day did not produce the evenness of torque desired when directly connected propellers were used and flywheels eliminated; demands for greater power also made necessary an increase in the number of cylinders. By 1912, a list of engines numbered 112 types, of which 42 were verticals, 24, 4-cylinder, and 16, 6-cylinder. By the beginning of World War I, most of the vertical engines for aviation use were 6- or 8-cylinder designs. Among American manufacturers of this type were Curtiss, Sturtevant, Kirkham, Christofferson, Aeromarine, Duesenberg, Wisconsin, Maximotor, Hall-Scott and Elbridge.

An early improvement over the vertical type in the layout of aviation powerplants was the vee engine. Power could be as much as doubled with, at most, only a slight increase in crankshaft length. The early vee-type engine usually had 8 cylinders, although others were made with 16 and even 32 cylinders. More even torque was transferred to the propeller than could be done by the upright engines, and designers found it easier to reduce crankshaft vibration.

A vee-type engine that enjoyed great popularity in French aviation for several years beginning about 1908 was the Antoinette, designed by Léon Levasseur. Somewhat earlier, he had built engines rated up to 8 hp. for use in motorboat racing. His best known aviation engines were rated at 50 hp. and had 8 cylinders. The aluminum crankcase was cast in the form of a rectangular prism, with the two rows of cylinders having an angle of 90° between them. In the earlier models, Levasseur used iron cylinders cast individually, with separate heads and copper jackets; beginning in 1909, he made the cylinders of steel, with integral heads and valve pockets. The two rows of cylinders were slightly offset in relation to one another, so that the two connecting rods of the opposed cylinders could be tied to a single, five-bearing crankshaft. Fuel was fed by direct injection, and lubrication was by a gear-driven pump. Cooling water turned to steam in the cylinder jackets, condensed in aluminum or copper tubes along the forward fuselage, and then was pumped back to the copper cylinder jackets. Although rated at 50 hp., the 1908 Antoinette engine could produce 67 hp. for takeoff. Bore was 4.3 in. and stroke 4.1 in. The engine operated at 1,100 rpm., and its dry weight was only 209 pounds.

In the United States, it was Glenn H. Curtiss (*see Chapters IX and* X) who pioneered in the design of the vee-type engine. His first 8-cylinder engine was built in 1909, especially for the successful effort to win the race for the Gordon Bennett Cup. Bore and stroke each measured 3¾ in. The engine ran at 1,100 rpm., and weighed about 200 lb., dry. Water-cooled, this power plant was the direct ancestor of a line of dependable engines, the most famous of which was the OX-5. More than 9,000 of this, the last of the series, were built; they powered the airplanes, notably the Jenny, that were used in training 10,000 World War I pilots. For years after the war, OX-5 engines continued in wide use.

As early as 1912, the 8-cylinder vee-type Curtiss Model O engine was producing 80 hp., and that year, further improvements were made to bring its rating up to 90 hp. at 1,400 rpm., although by modification of the valve gear, much greater output was frequently obtained for racing purposes. The new engine was to have been designated O + but there was a mistake made and it came out OX!

The two banks of cylinders had a 90° angle. Bore was 4 in. and stroke 5 in. The crankshaft had five bearings, and the connecting rods were mounted side by side. The cast iron cylinders had Monel-metal water jackets, and the overhead valves were operated by two concentric push rods. The inner rod operated the exhaust valve through large rockers, and the outer rod, worked by a powerful spring and an aluminum rocker arm, pulled the inlet valve open at the proper time. Especially for the state of the engine art of the time, the cam and push rod design was ingenious, and the whole valve construction very light. Fuel consumption was .6 lb/hp./hr.

Another, larger Curtiss vee-type engine, development of which began in 1913, was the Model V. With a bore of 5 in. and a stroke of 7 in., the V-2 version had cylinders of drawn steel, with a steel water jacket top and a Monel metal cylindrical jacket, both of which were brazed to the cylinder barrel. The original V had 8 cylinders and was rated at 160 hp. at 1,400 rpm. The V-2, also with 8 cylinders, gave 220 hp. A 12-cylinder model, the V-3, was originally rated at 250 hp., but actually gave about 300 hp. at 1,500 rpm.

Among early European manufacturers of vee-type aviation engines was the Renault firm in France, which employed a fan and shrouding to obtain air-cooling. In 1910, Renault was building three sizes of 8-cylinder engines, and by 1915, five sizes, ranging from 25 to 100 hp. The largest of the Renault engines, still air-cooled, had 12 cylinders. Panhard and Levassor and de Dion also built vee-type engines in France. In Great Britain, where aero engine development lagged behind other European countries" prior to World War I, the Wolseley company and the Dorman firm built early vee-type engines. In the United States, Sturtevant, Hall-Scott, Wisconsin, and Thomas Morse were among those to build vee-type engines prior to World War I. During the War, the Allies depended largely upon vee-type designs—the Rolls Royce Eagle, the Hispano-Suiza and the Liberty, to mention three—while the Germans and Austrians concentrated upon vertical-type engines, especially those manufactured by Mercedes-Benz.

Still another of the types of aviation engine manufactured in the early years was the radial. Its first construction for aerial use was actually in the form of a half-radial, but until the first World War, the obvious advantages of the air-cooled radial continued to attract attention. This type, as it was developed in France, came directly from motorcycle engine practice. If one excepts the Langley-Manly radial engine, which was never afforded a real opportunity to demonstrate its value in aeronautics, then the first truly successful example of the type was the 3-cylinder Anzani. Its builder was Alessandro Anzani, an Italian with shops at Asnieres, a suburb of Paris. The principal product of the Anzani works had been a 2-cylinder, air-cooled motorcycle engine. The 3-cylinder power plant was first built in 1908, so the story goes, to meet the requirements of a German road racer for more power. At any rate, the new engine came to the attention of Louis Bleriot, and when he flew the English Channel on July 25, 1909, with the engine installed, the popularity of the Anzani was assured.

In the earliest of the Anzani engines, one finned cast iron cylinder was vertical, with the other two positioned at an angle of 72° on each side, thus to avoid the possibility of over-lubrication of the bottom cylinders. Weights were fitted inside the crankcase to overcome the unequal balance which resulted. Anzani's first engines weighed about 110 pounds, and were hopefully rated at 25 hp. at 1,200 rpm.

Later versions of the 3-cylinder Anzani had a Y-type arrangement, with the cylinders 120° apart. The bore was 4.1 in. and the stroke was 4.7 in. At 1,300 rpm., 30 hp. developed. Anzani rapidly built more powerful radials, and by 1914 his firm was constructing seven sizes, the largest of which had 20 cylinders and was essentially a double radial. Fuel consumption was only .49 lb./hp./hr., but oil consumption was very high, being as much as one-fifth the rate of fuel burned. In the United States, the 6-cylinder Albatross, made in two sizes, was produced in small numbers before World War I; it was a close copy of the Anzani.

Another of the semi-radial engines was built in the early years of aviation by Robert Esnault-Pelterie, who was also known for his innovations in airplane design. His was a 7-cylinder, air-cooled power plant, with the cylinders positioned fan-shape on the upper part of the crankcase, four in front and three to the rear. The crankcase was an aluminum alloy casting; the cylinders were cast iron, and the pistons, steel. Two crankshafts were used. Bore was 3.3 in., and stroke was 3.5 in. At 1,500 rpm., the R.E.P. engine was rated at 30 hp., and its total operating weight was only 115 lb.

At the relatively low speeds of airplanes prior to 1914, cooling proved to be a discouraging problem. In order to save weight, the sections of the cast iron pistons were made too thin for proper heat distribution, and power output was low, especially in comparison with the best efforts of the water-cooled vee-types. One solution was to provide water cooling for the radial type. The Canton-Unné (Salmson) engines were among the most popular of the radials with water cooling. In 1914, six sizes were being built. The 9-cylinder model produced 130 hp. Cylinders were machined of nickel steel, with spun copper water jackets brazed to the cylinders. Ball bearings were used extensively. The Salmson engine was built in France and under license in Great Britain.

One of the most interesting of the early aviation engines, one which enjoyed a great popularity for several years, was the Gnome rotary, designed and built by the Seguin brothers, Laurent and Louis. First shown publicly at the Rheims meet in 1909, it was used initially to power Voisin and Farman airplanes. In the latter, Louis Paulhan won the London-Manchester race in 1910; his closest competitor, Claude Grahame-White, flew a similarly powered Farman, so quickly had the Gnome become accepted. In the rotary engine, the crankshaft was stationary, with the cylinders and crankcase revolving. Among advantages were the evenness of torque and also the comparative effectiveness of the air cooling, resulting from the rotation of the cylinders. To be sure, cooling was uneven, with one side of the cylinders being cooled more than the other, resulting in a tendency to distortion. The consumption of lubricating oil was excessive. In the case of the 100 hp. Gnome, oil consumption was estimated by the manufacturer at 7 pints an hour, but in actual use this amount often was greatly exceeded. Despite these disadvantages, the Gnome was liked because it was dependable to a degree quite uncommon in the years before World War I.

The earliest of the Gnome engines had 5 cylinders and produced 34 hp. at 1,300 rpm.; it was soon displaced by a 7-cylinder model that developed up to 67 hp. Within a year, the Seguin brothers were building three types of Gnome engines, 9- and 14-cylinder versions in addition to the original 7-cylinder power plant. Some 75 per cent of the parts of the 7-cylinder engine could be used in the 14-cylinder type which, effectively, was a double-size version of the smaller. Most of the Gnome engine parts were made from nickel steel. The cylinders were machined from solid bar stock until wall thickness was hardly 1/16 in., with the cooling fins being ground out. Bore was 4.3 in. and stroke was 4.7 in. The crankcase was not unlike a steel hoop, while the steel crankshaft was hollow, with gasoline and lubricating oil passing through it to the cylinders by centrifugal action. Castor oil was used for lubrication because it was not cut by gasoline as much as mineral oil.

By 1914, more than 40 types and sizes of rotary engines were being manufactured. The Seguin factory had introduced an improved, Monosoupape (single valve) model. Other European manufacturers of rotaries included LeRhone and Clerget in France, and the Bayerische Motoren Werke in Germany. For a brief time in 1911, the Hendee Manufacturing Company of Springfield, Mass., undertook construction of a rotary similar in virtually every respect to the 50-hp. Gnome. During the war years, both the Gnome and LeRhone engines were built in quantity in the United States. Because of the large centrifugal forces created by the revolving engine mass, 1,400 rpm. was a practical operating limit, and consequently, the rotary lost out in the war years to the vee-type, as more and more power was developed by the latter type.

There were still other engine types in this early period, but space permits passing mention of only two. Santos-Dumont's tiny Demoiselle was powered by a 2-cylinder, horizontally opposed Darracq engine that was water-cooled and developed nearly 24 hp. In a sense, this powerplant was the grand-daddy of the air-cooled, horizontal opposed engines that have powered most of the tens of thousands of light planes built in the past 30 years.

The small engines built by the Darracq and Duthiel-Chalmers firms were similar in most respects. The smallest Darracq model, rated at 24 hp. at 1,500 rpm., had a bore of 5.1 in. and a stroke of 4.7 in., while the Duthiel-Chalmers model, with a bore of 5 in. and a stroke of 5.1 in., produced 25 hp. Each engine weighed about 120 lb. In France, the Clément-Bayard company also built opposed-cylinder engines, both air- and water-cooled. In the United States, the Ashmusen 6-cylinder horizontal engine was rated at 100 hp., the largest of the pre-war power plants of the type.

Although 4-cycle engines were predominant, there were examples of 2-cycle engine construction. In the United States were the Fredericson, a 5-cylinder rotary rated at 70 hp., and the 6-cylinder vertical Roberts engines, producing up to 100 hp. The Roberts engine was built in some numbers.

The talents of the early aviation engine designers, even when considered in the light of progress made in the 50 and more years since, were many. To be sure, in 1914 the internal combustion aviation engine was only at the threshold of its development. But the work that remained to be done was largely, as the research man is apt to say and the hard-pushed designer is just as likely to resent, a matter of sufficient, straightforward, engineering effort. Great strides in metallurgy and shop practice made possible construction of lighter, stronger, more reliable engines. Increased knowledge about heat transfer or, if you will, cooling, was similarly important. And so, of course, were the development of supercharging methods to help the engine breathe more efficiently, and of better fuels.

The fact remains:—It is not too much to say that, basically, all the internal-combustion aviation engines built since 1914 have been the logical development of their forerunners.

# 15/ THE FIRST MILITARY AIRPLANES

*The sky is changed,—and such a change! O night*
*And storm, and darkness! Ye are wondrous strong,*
*Yet lovely in your strength, as is the light*
*Of a dark eye in woman! Far along,*
*From peak to peak, the rattling crags among,*
*Leaps the live thunder.*

BYRON

For centuries it had been known, "he that commands the sea is at great liberty," and upon close attention to this truth, great empires had been built, the most recent the British. So had it been known for at least as long that the air and its command held possibilities of conquest, even greater and more absolute.

Early, Wilbur and Orville Wright sensed that the quality about their airplane that gave it great value was its potential as a military vehicle. In 1905, they expressed this awareness in a letter to Capt. Ferdinand Ferber of the French Army: "We have used the entire last year in completing our machine and we little thought what we would do with it when it was ready. But our present view is to offer it first to the governments for war purposes and if you believe that your government might be interested in it, we would gladly get in touch with it."

Again they wrote the French captain in November of 1905: "With Russia and Austria-Hungary in their present troubled condition and the German Emperor in a truculent mood, a spark may produce an explosion at any minute. No government dare take the risk of waiting to develop practical flying machines independently."

As has been related (*see Chapter VI*) the governments of the world were indeed interested in the Wright airplane for war purposes. Such a statement, however, requires qualification; the interest was, perhaps, somewhat tentative. Granted that the airplane offered possibilities, especially in the matter of reconnaissance, what about performance and reliability?

Too, in the early days of the Twentieth Century, the chiefs of staff, the makers of policy in warlike matters of the great nations, were confronted with the need for assimilating into their plans other new elements for use on the day when, traditionally, the troops would march and the *uhlans*, the *chasseurs*, and the lancers would wheel and ride forward to strike brave blows for a righteous cause. On land, there was the automobile which threatened to smash the logistic calculations based upon movement of troops by foot and horse-drawn van. Beneath the sea there was the submarine, an invention with frightening possibilities that after a century of slow development now seemed likely to be realized. In the air, there was poison gas to wreak invisible havoc upon all in the path of the onrushing winds.

Yes, after Wilbur and Orville Wright first flew, the generals and the admirals had much in the way of technological advances to ponder. It is perhaps easy, more than a half century later, to understand how massive were the decisions the military planners were called upon to make. The implications of learning how to use the automobile, the submarine, and poison gas—and the airplane—to supplement the capabilities of land armies and ships of the line were no less difficult to comprehend than the problems of those leaders of a later day who faced such questions as whether, when and how to replace manned airplanes with intercontinental ballistic missiles, and orbiting satellites.

Bleriot's crossing of the English Channel in July, 1909 (*see Chapter VIII*) has been widely accepted as the dramatic event which aroused British interest in the military possibilities of aviation. This doubtless is true, at least in the sense that the Channel crossing served to accelerate aeronautical development in Great Britain. Elsewhere in Europe, especially in France and Germany, efforts already were being made along those lines, but never so rapidly or to the extent desired by the enthusiasts.

Ironically—in the light of the relative inattention to aviation matters in the United States—first military use of the airplane was in America, early in 1911. In that year there was revolutionary trouble in Mexico, and US Army personnel were stationed along the border to guard against forays across the line by either loyalists or insurgents. First used for observation purposes was a Wright biplane loaned by Robert J. Collier. This gesture by the sportsman was well timed because the one military plane then Lt. Benjamin D. Foulois, USA, had at his disposal in Texas was about to be shipped back to the Wright factory for major overhaul and repair.

With Foulois serving as observer, Philip O. Parmalie, a pilot in the employ of the Wright brothers, flew the Collier airplane on several reconnaissance missions near Laredo. Foulois carried a carbine for "defense." On at least one occasion, the plane was fitted with wireless. Aerial photographs also were taken. Not long after the start of the aerial reconnaissance, a forced landing in the Rio Grande River damaged the Wright airplane badly.

At about the same time Harry Harkness made similar flights in the San Diego-Tijuana area, using an Antoinette monoplane. Charles Hamilton also flew his biplane across the Rio Grande at El Paso, and passed over Ciudad Juarez, at that time under siege by the insurgents.

Later in 1911 Bleriot, Nieuport and Etrich monoplanes were used in the Italo-Turkish war for observation, bomb dropping, and spotting gun fire. The bombs used by the Italians were described as being about the size and shape of a big orange, with a loading plug below and a fuse on top. The spotting of gun fire—information is lacking as to its success—took place on October 26 during the battle of Sciara-Sciat. Two airplanes were used by the Italians in connection with the firing of mountain artillery and also of the big guns of the *Carlo Alberto*.

What was perhaps the first official military communique to mention airplane use was issued November 5, 1911, in Tripoli, as follows: "Yesterday Capts. Moizo, Piazza, and DeRada carried out an airplane reconnaissance, DeRada successfully trying a new Farman military biplane. Moizo, after locating the position of the enemy's battery, flew over Ain Zara, and dropped two bombs into the Arab encampment. He found that the enemy were much diminished in numbers since he saw them last time. Piazza dropped two bombs on the enemy with effect. The object of the reconnaissance was to discover the headquarters of the Arab and Turkish troops."

About the same time, the Italian pilots learned from experience that if they flew as low as 500 feet, thus to make more detailed observations, they became vulnerable to rifle fire from the ground. One pilot found upon landing that the fabric of his Nieuport had been pierced by six bullets. On February 1, 1912, a Capt. Montu of the Italian military air corps was severely wounded in flight at an altitude of about 1,800 feet by gunfire from an Arabian encampment he was observing near Tobruk. In those days, most of the effort was devoted to the basic job of designing and building airplanes that would provide reasonable speed, range, and dependability. To have concentrated more upon the obvious further step of changing the design of airplanes especially for military use doubtless would have resulted in a task too difficult, too complicated.

Nevertheless, some modification was made of existing types to improve military usefulness. At the same time, accessory equipment was being perfected. In 1910, the French made tests with a light machine gun (*mitrailleuse*) installed on a Voisin biplane. In 1911, the fuselages of Farman biplanes were "armored" by application of thin metal sheets. Use of wireless installed in airplanes was under active development. The year following, the well-known German scientific instrument firm of Zeiss patented a bomb-sighting device. It was described as incorporating an inverted theodolite and a chronometer, and claims of substantial improvement in accuracy resulting from its use were made. Use was begun also of oxygen to permit pilots to fly higher. In the United States, in 1912, the new rapid-fire, air-cooled machine gun of Lt. Col. I. N. Lewis, US Coast Artillery, was given aerial trials.

That same year, the French journal *L'Aero* speculated about the advantage, if any, possible in the relative positions of two airplanes, one the pursuer, and the other the pursued. "Assuming that the two airplanes be flying at the same speed, the same altitude and with equal armament, one pursuing the other; which, the pursuer or the pursued, can damage the other with the least risk of being itself damaged?" The magazine's answer was that the fleeing airplane would have all the best of it. "Taking into consideration the nature of the projectile most likely to be discharged from airplanes, it was concluded that the fleeing airplane would scarcely sustain serious damage even if hit . . . This was the opinion not only of officers of the army and navy, and of gunnery experts, but renowned mathematicians reached the same conclusions through considerations of a theoretical nature."

Before turning attention to the manner of airplane improvement between 1910 and the outbreak of World War I in 1914, note may be made of experiments conducted in 1911, carrying the mail by air. The first of these endeavors took place, not in Great Britain or in the United States as might be supposed, but in India. The date was February 18, and the occasion was the exhibition at Allahabad. Several thousand letters were carried, over a period of days, the five mile distance from the exhibition grounds to the receiving station at Naini across the Jumna river. The plane used was a Humber biplane (a British version of the Farman) powered by a Humber engine. Capt. W. G. Windham and M. H. Piquet were the pilots.

On September 9, 1911, in Great Britain, air mail service was provided for about two weeks over the 20 miles between Hendon and Windsor. Three planes, two Bleriot monoplanes and a Farman biplane, were used to carry more than 100,000 cards and letters in this feature of the coronation festivities for King George V. On one flight, a tail wind made possible a speed of 105 mph.; on another trip, the pilot took 90 minutes because he had lost his way.

In the United States, beginning September 23, 1911, mail was carried by air from Nassau Boulevard to Mineola and Garden City, Long Island, distances of less than 10 miles each. Capt. Paul W. Beck, USA, carried Postmaster General Frank Hitchcock and mail to Mineola in a Curtiss biplane. Earle L. Ovington flew a Queen monoplane (an American-built copy of a Bleriot powered by an Indian rotary engine) on similar missions to Nassau Boulevard. Again, thousands of cards and letters were carried; again the accomplishment was a stunt, staged to publicize an air meet. Regularly scheduled carriage of mail by airplane, over distances that had meaning, was still to come. As a matter of fact, for several years, perhaps as late as 1911, the designers of airplanes had reason for satisfaction if their craft could be coaxed at all into the air. In France especially it seemed everyone was determined to produce a model that would be different from all others and thus bear unmistakably the imprint of its owner. In mid-summer of 1911, the list of entries for the trials conducted by the French military authorities included no less than two-score names, beginning with Antoinette, Astra and Bebin . . . and continuing through the alphabet to Timaskian, Verdier and Zodiac. The appearance of not a few of these offerings was strange and wonderful.

So far as performance was concerned—especially in the matter of speed—the tractor monoplane early showed itself susceptible to greatest improvement. At the same time, the number of pilots killed in single-wing craft rose rapidly, and soon there was widespread criticism of the type.

In France, Edouard and Charles Nieuport were among the most successful of the pioneer monoplane designers. In 1910, they built a monoplane that was powered by a 20-hp. flat twin-cylinder engine of their own design. The monoplane was capable of almost 80 mph.; its fuselage was made of steel tubing, with fabric covering. The Nieuport brothers were among the first to use streamline forms effectively to reduce drag. In 1911, C. T. Weyman, an American, won the Gordon Bennett trophy in a Nieuport. Weyman's speed was 78 mph.; he used a 100-hp. Gnome-rotary engine. Edouard Nieuport was killed in 1911, and Charles in 1913, the latter in a three-seater powered by a 100-hp. Gnome-rotary. The name, however, was continued on the roll of airplane manufacturers well beyond World War I, by the Société Anonyme des Etablissements Nieuport.

Léon and Robert Morane were another team of French brothers to build well-known monoplanes. In 1910 in a Bleriot, Léon had been the first to fly faster than 100 kilometers an hour (62.14 mph.). With his brother, he built fast monoplanes that soon won attention. Later Raymond Saulnier joined the Morane brothers; his engineering competence contributed importantly to subsequent designs, among them the monoplane Roland Garros flew in 1912 to a height of 18,400 feet, a world's record. Large numbers of Morane-

Saulnier monoplanes were built for service in both world wars.

Among the most successful of the monoplane constructors was the Deperdussin firm which made use of the far-sighted design talents of M. L. Béchereau. Among the first of the high-performance Deperdussin airplanes was the one built in 1910. Its fuselage had a very small cross-section, and it was powered by a 40-hp. 4-cylinder Clerget engine.

By 1912, the Béchereau-designed Deperdussins were the fastest airplanes of the day. In that year at Chicago, Jules Védrines and Maurice Prévost, flying Deperdussins, finished first and second in the Gordon Bennett race. Védrines averaged 105 mph. over the 125 miles, and Prévost was only slightly slower.

The span of the wing of the 1912 racer was 23 feet, with the taper outboard like that of a butterfly; wing area was 100 square feet. Spars were of hickory and ribs of pine and ash. The 20-foot, 6-inch fuselage was of monocoque construction with a lattice gridwork covered by a shell of three-ply wood. The tailplane had 15 square feet of surface, the elevators 10 square feet, and the rudder 4 square feet. The 7-foot, 9-inch tractor propeller was driven by a 14-cylinder 100-hp. Gnome rotary engine which was cowled by thin aluminum sheet. Wing-warping was used on this racer which had a landing speed of almost 90 mph.

The same year the Deperdussin firm built a two-place monoplane for military use. It had a 39-foot, 6-inch wingspan with 236 square feet of area, and the fuselage measured 24 feet 6 inches. The empennage surfaces measured 39, 19, and 5 square feet, respectively, for the tail, elevators, and rudder. The forward part of the fuselage was protected by aluminum sheeting. Wing-warping was used for the pre-war Deperdussin military models as well as for the racers. A British version of the military Deperdussin resembled closely the French model; Fritz Koolhoven (later to become well known for his own radical models that were built in Holland) was in charge of its design.

Again in 1913, a Béchereau-designed Deperdussin won the Gordon Bennet race, held that year at Rheims. Prévost was the pilot of the racer, which resembled the 1912 model. The improvements included a 160-hp. Gnome rotary engine, fuselage streamlining behind the pilot's head used for the first time, streamlined landing-gear struts, and a larger spinner covering the hub of the 7-foot, 7-inch Chauviere propeller. It was in this airplane that Prévost was first to fly 200 kilometers (124.28 miles) within an hour. Three years previously, Claude Grahame-White in a clipped-wing Bleriot was the first to fly 100 kilometers (62.14 miles) in one hour, one minute. The 1913 Deperdussin racer had a wing span of 21 feet 10 inches and a fuselage length of 20 feet.

In 1913 the Deperdussin company suffered difficulties and was put in the hands of a receiver. In World War I its products, still designed by Béchereau, were famous—the biplane Spads (Société pour Production les Appareils Deperdussin had been changed to Société pour Aviation et ses Derives). In later years, Louis Bleriot was active in the affairs of the organization building the Spads.

In the years before World War I, the Germans also showed partiality for the monoplane design, especially for the flying-leaf (*zanonia*) wing type which provided a large degree of inherent stability. The Etrich and Rumpler monoplanes—in fact, most of the German single-wing designs—were of this type. They became generally known as the *Taube* or Pigeon type. Other German monoplane constructors of the period included Grade, Schultze, Jeannin, and Harland.

Ernst Heinkel designed several fast monoplanes which were built by L.V.G. and by Albatros; these craft were much closer to the French Nieuport than the German Taube in appearance. Finally, for the Germans, there was the young Dutchman, Anthony Fokker, whose monoplane was bought by the military not long before the beginning of World War I.

In Great Britain the monoplane never enjoyed the widespread favor it found in France and Germany. This statement can be made despite the fact that at one time or another before 1914, most of the leading British experimenters turned out one or more monoplanes, and monoplanes built in France were purchased in some numbers. Robert Blackburn, Frederick Handley Page, and A. V. Roe were among those to build monoplanes. Bristol used monoplane designs supplied by Pierre Prier and Henri Coanda, both of France, and even one of the first of J. W. Dunne's inherently stable, swept-wing aircraft was a monoplane.

But, as has been indicated above, many pilots were killed in monoplanes, especially in France and Great Britain, and the type became the target of widespread criticism. The matter came to a spectacular climax in France in the spring of 1912 when Louis Bleriot, probably the best known of all the pioneer monoplane designers, sent a communication to the French government. In his message, Bleriot said in as many words that air loads on the top of the wing were much greater than had been suspected, and that by adequate trussing with guy wires, the accidents peculiar to monoplane design could be eliminated. Earlier, the unsuccessful efforts to cut down on monoplane accidents had for the most part been concentrated upon strengthening the wing spars.

Bleriot's comments resulted in the War Minister suspending the use of monoplanes by the French army, pending re-trussing of the wings along the lines suggested. His action was widely hailed for its courage although there were some, among them Mervyn O'Gorman of the British Royal Aircraft Factory, who declined to accept the Bleriot explanation of top pressure as being technically correct. "It belongs to the order of speech which may be called chatty," O'Gorman observed, adding, "For all that, he deserves credit for pointing out a great risk." About this time, Bleriot also encouraged the spectacular aerobatics of Adolphe Pégoud, generally credited with having been the first to loop the loop in 1913. (The Frenchman Chanteloup and the Russian Nesterov also have been cited as the first to loop.) His gyrations served, it was felt, as dramatic proof of the basic soundness of the Bleriot monoplane design. In France, the rigging changes recommended by Bleriot were promptly made, and the monoplane continued to enjoy favor, due in no small part to its superior speed.

In Great Britain, fatal accidents involving monoplanes continued for several months, and in the summer of 1912 the British War Office forbade further use of the type pending an official inquiry. The findings of the committee, published in February of the next year, failed to condemn the monoplane as a type—stating, rather, that no reason had been found to prohibit the use of monoplanes, providing certain precautions were taken, some of them applicable both to monoplanes and biplanes. Despite the findings, from then on the War Office showed little enthusiasm for additional purchases of monoplanes. Thus, in England, the biplane was given an advantage so definite that decades would pass before the monoplane regained favor in that country.

German monoplanes suffered troubles but of a different sort. In 1913 the Army insisted that airplanes be capable of quick and easy disassembly to permit ready loading on wagons or trucks for cross-country transport. One of the Rumpler Taubes was equipped with wings built sectionally to facilitate the speedy disassembly desired. While being flown by two Army officers, the wing broke apart and both men were killed. The accident aroused considerable criticism in Germany against the monoplane. But in the last analysis it was the success of the German airplane industry in developing large, sturdy biplanes with all-around superiority (excepting speed) that most surely lessened the popularity of the monoplane, especially for military use.

The relative ease with which adequate strength could be designed into a Pratt truss type of structure—an advantage which Chanute and the Wright brothers had recognized—continued to be an important factor favoring the biplane throughout the first decade of powered flight. Construction techniques still were crude. Lightweight alloys of high strength, such as the Dural that Alfred Wilm had invented in Germany about 1909, were as yet unproved. If speed was not the paramount consideration, then the biplane could be expected to give a good account of itself.

In France in the days before the war, the principal adherents to the biplane included a trio of brothers, Henri and Maurice Farman, Gaston and René Caudron, and Charles and Gabriel Voisin. Their airplanes were slow when compared with contemporary monoplanes, but they were relatively reliable because it was possible for their biplanes, with larger lifting surfaces, to carry greater loads.

The Farman brothers designed individually, but joined forces for construction economies. From 1909 through 1913, with but a single exception, their pusher biplanes held the world's records both for endurance and distance around a closed circuit (it was not until after the war that the Federation Aéronautique Internationale recognized straight-line distance records). The single exception was the closed circuit distance record in 1911, established that year by a Nieuport monoplane that was flown 460 miles.

In 1909 the duration record stood at 4 hours 17 minutes, with a Henri Farman biplane. By 1913 a Maurice Farman biplane had been flown nonstop for 13 hours, 22 minutes. The 1909 closed circuit distance record was made by a Henri Farman at 145 miles. By 1913, another of Henri's biplanes had been flown nonstop 634 miles.

Generally speaking, the biplanes of the Farman brothers were similar, except that the designs of Henri incorporated a single tail and rudder while Maurice used a double tail and rudder assembly. Perhaps the most primitive in appearance, to avoid use of the word *ugly,* was Maurice's Longhorn design. Despite the fact that the elevator was still mounted forward instead of aft with the tail, it had the tolerably good top speed of almost 60 mph. when powered by a 75-hp. Renault engine. The wing span was 51 feet, the fuselage length, 37 feet. The pilot and passenger rode in an enclosed nacelle with the engine. Uncovered fuselage booms extended back to the tail assembly. Weight empty was about 1,250 pounds; fully loaded, it was about 1,900 pounds. By the outbreak of the war it had been long surpassed in performance. Nonetheless, large numbers of the Longhorn design were used for pilot-training as late as 1916.

Maurice's Shorthorn design, which came out in 1913, was a trifle larger than the Longhorn (wing span was 53 feet) and about 10 per cent faster. The elevator had been moved aft, and the clumsy skid supporting the forward-mounted elevator was shortened greatly. Weight empty was about 1,500 pounds; fully loaded, it was about 2,000 pounds.

Henri's Model 20 was also built in 1913. Smaller than the pusher biplane designed by Maurice, it had a wing span of 45 feet and a fuselage length of 25 feet. An 80-hp. Gnome-rotary engine was used. Weight empty was hardly 800 pounds; fully loaded, it was about 1,400 pounds. Top speed was about the same as that of the Shorthorn. Whereas the Maurice Farman airplanes used wood construction throughout, with wire bracing, Henri's Model 20, in at least one version, used steel tubing for the tail booms.

Sons of a farm family, the Caudron brothers became interested early in aviation. By 1911, they had progressed to a point where their small biplane attracted considerable favorable attention at the annual Paris Salon. Although its planform was similar to the pusher type, with the tail supported by booms and the pilot and passenger seated in a nacelle, it was a tractor airplane with the 35-hp. Anzani air-cooled engine located in the nose of the nacelle. Typically, the lower wing of the Caudron designs was so much smaller than the upper as to warrant calling the airplanes sesquiplanes. The 1911 model, priced at $1,600 with a guaranteed speed of 55 mph., and a subsequent offering, powered by a 45-hp. Anzani, proved popular for schooling use both in France and England.

By early 1914 the Caudron brothers were delivering a two-place military model, the G-2. It had a span of 38 feet (total wing area was 300 square feet) and a fuselage length of 24 feet. Powered by an 80-hp. rotary engine (either Gnome or LeRhone) the biplane had a top speed of almost 70 mph. Weight empty was about 900 pounds; fully loaded, it was nearly 1,600 pounds. Built in quantity, this airplane was used extensively in the early part of the war.

The Voisin Brothers, who started constructing airplanes on a custom basis to the design of others (*see Chapter VIII*), concentrated upon the conventional pusher-type biplane. Their success, which carried well into the war years, may be credited largely to high quality workmanship plus painstaking attention to detail. Fuselage and wing construction employed both wood and steel, with the booms to the tail assembly of steel. The upper and lower wings were of the same dimension, and the span was 44 feet, with wing area, 452 square feet. Fuselage length was 31 feet. Weight empty was 1,300 pounds; fully loaded, it was 1,900 pounds. An 80-hp. rotary engine was used, with Gnome, LeRhone and Clerget sharing the power plant production. Speed was hardly 60 mph.

In Great Britain aircraft development was furthered by two main forces, the Royal Aircraft Factory at Farnborough and private designers. Respecting the biplane, both groups gave attention not only to the pusher type but also to tractor designs. For the most part, the products of the Factory were favored by the War Office, while the Admiralty looked to private contractors for its machines.

Between 1911 and the outbreak of the war, the Factory developed three types of military airplane. In the last months before the beginning of the conflict, a fourth type was brought forward. Each type had a two-letter designation, followed by the number indicating position in the series. B.E. stood for Bleriot Experimental, in deference to Bleriot's pioneering use of a tractor design. The other types were F.E., Farman Experimental; S.E., Scouting Experimental, and R.E., Reconnaissance Experimental.

The first of these Factory-produced airplanes to be successful was the B.E. 2, which was probably the best of the Britain airplanes in 1912. Designed by Geoffrey de Havilland (who soon went on to organize his own company), the B.E. 2 distinguished itself both by its climbing capabilities and by its good, all-around flying qualities. Powered by a 70-hp. Renault air-cooled engine, it had a top speed of about 70 mph. Its span was 38 feet (wing area, 374 square feet) and its fuselage was 29 feet long. Both wing and fuselage construction were of wood, with wire bracing. The wood struts between the wings were streamlined; beginning with the B.E. 2c, the wings were staggered. Weight empty was about 1,300 pounds; fully loaded, it was about 1,900 pounds. Before the end of the type, several thousand B.E.'s were built.

Neither the F.E. series (patterned after the Farman pushers) nor the S.E. airplanes were spectacular performers, but both types were steadily improved to the point where large numbers were ultimately used. The R.E. series is of special interest because of its high degree of inherent stability; incorporated in the design of the R.E. 1 were aerodynamic theories of F. W. Lanchester (*see Chapter XIII*) and G. H. Bryan. Leonard Bairstow and others at the National Physical Laboratory also worked on the design, at first employing models to prove their theories. E. T. Busk, who performed much of the flight test program, had a sound technical background and well may have been the first of the engineer test pilots. Again, later variants of the R.E. series were built in quantity during the war. By then, however, maneuverability and speed were qualities more greatly preferred than inherent stability.

One of the first of the "private" British designs to win lasting popularity was the 504 which A. V. Roe built in the summer of

1913. In September of that year, it finished fourth, with a speed of 66 mph., in a cross-country race of 95 miles. First and second were a pair of monoplanes; the Avro biplane entry was within a minute of the third-placing Sopwith biplane. In November the Avro 504 passed the flight test program at Farnborough, being timed (perhaps aided by a puff or two of wind) at 80 mph. Its stalling speed of 43 mph. was highly regarded, especially for flight training. The wings of the Avro 504 were staggered; span was 36 feet, and area was 342 square feet. Fuselage length was 29 feet, and the area of the tail surfaces was 42 square feet. A Gnome-rotary of 80 hp. was used. Empty weight was 1,100 pounds; fully loaded, it was 1,800 pounds.

Although the Avro 504 was used on military missions in the early days of the war (three 504's were flown by Navy pilots November 21, 1914 on one of the war's first bombing missions, against the German Zeppelin works at Friedrichshafen) the airplane's principal assignment was pilot training. In all, some 17,000 Avro 504's were built; the only basic changes made over the years of production were those necessary to accommodate more powerful engines. For years after the war, with the Curtiss "Jenny," the Avro 504 continued to be widely used.

Another 1913 British airplane to enjoy success, one which marked a large advance in the state of the art, was the Sopwith Tabloid. Fred Segrist contributed importantly to the design of the Tabloid, as he did with a number of later airplanes produced by T. O. M. Sopwith. Originally constructed as a side-by-side two-seater with wing warping, the Tabloid as built for military sale was a single-seater scout, equipped with ailerons. Although the design was straightforward, with the fuselage essentially a square section that tapered to a knife edge at the tail, it was remarkably clean for the day. For the first time, a single set of streamlined struts was used on each side of the fuselage. The 80-hp. Gnome engine was beautifully cowled, with only two slit openings for cooling air. Wing span was 25 feet 6 inches and area was 230 square feet; the lower wing was staggered aft about a foot. Fuselage length was only 20 feet. Weight empty of the military version was about 700 pounds; fully loaded, it was about 1,200 pounds.

Performance of the Sopwith Tabloid—ancestor of a line of Scouts to bear the company name—included a top speed better than 90 mph., a stalling speed less than 40 mph., and a climbing capability of 1,200 feet per minute. In short, this little biplane could out-perform all but the fastest of the racing monoplanes. In retrospect, the Tabloid perhaps more than any other must be credited with convincing the British military officials of the rightness of their preference for the biplane.

Two other British pre-war biplanes deserve mention. Soon after the appearance of the Tabloid, the British and Colonial Airplane Company brought out the Bristol Scout, which became known as the Bullet. In performance and appearance this design by Henri Coanda was similar to that of the Sopwith airplane. It proved itself in a number of races just before the war, and several hundred were constructed for military use. Also brought out at the end of 1913 was the Vickers pusher biplane that became known as the Gun Bus. Powered by a 100-hp. Gnome *monosoupape* (single valve) engine, it had a top speed of about 70 mph. The Gun Bus proved to be a worthy opponent of the Fokker "Eindekker" at a time when such opposition was badly needed.

In Germany, vigorous development of the biplane came somewhat later than in Great Britain. In the early days, most German biplanes were reasonably close copies of the Farman designs. It was not until 1912 that, prodded by the Army, German designers came forward with the first of the biplanes foreshadowing the aircraft that would be most used in the early part of the war. A factor important to the success of these German biplanes was the power plant. The Mercedes and Benz factories began producing water-cooled, 6-cylinder, in-line engines sufficiently powerful and reliable to assure relatively good performance by the heavier biplanes.

Ernst Heinkel made large contributions to the improvement of German biplane design practice beginning in 1912, although he admitted partiality for the monoplane type because of its greater speed potential. In 1912 he designed the military biplane that L.V.G. (Luft Verkehrs Gesellschaft) built for the Army. The following spring, he moved to the Albatros Works where he designed the biplane that won the 1913 military competition. It was so laid out that wings of different span could be used for such varying purposes as high altitude flight, transport, and general military use.

In 1913 and '14, German aircraft companies producing biplanes for military use, in addition to L.V.G. and Albatros, included Aviatik, D.F.W. (Deutsche Flugzeug Werke), A.E.G. (Allgemeine Elektrizitats Gessellschaft), and the Hansa-Brandenburgische Flugzeugwerke (which absorbed the German airplane factory of Etrich and to which Heinkel had gone in 1914). The airplanes were remarkably similar in layout. Wing span varied from about 37 feet to 46 feet, and fuselage length from 27 feet to 30 feet. Weight empty was 1,200 to 1,400 pounds; fully loaded, it was 2,100 to 2,400 pounds.

How well the Germans were learning to design and build biplanes may be seen from the records they established in 1914 before outbreak of the war in August. Hellmuth Hirth, and Ritter and Edler von Lössel, flying Albatros military models, set progressively higher altitude marks in the passenger-carrying categories, reaching above 15,000 feet. Far more spectacular, however, was Reinhold Oelrich's flight in a D.F.W., powered by a 100-hp. Mercedes engine, to a height of 25,780 feet, more than a mile higher than the previous altitude record.

On June 27, 1914, Werner Landmann smashed the endurance record, flying nonstop for 21 hours and 49 minutes. Two weeks later, Reinhold Böhm bettered this mark with a time of 24 hours, 12 minutes. Both flights were in Albatros machines. Although they were not officially recognized as record breaking by the F.A.I. for technical reasons, the nonstop flights, each longer than 1,200 miles, by Ernst Stöffler in an Aviatik and Landmann in an Albatros, were equally impressive. Admittedly, all these were flights with airplanes specially groomed for a specific performance goal; nevertheless, the way was pointed clearly to what would be done not long after by standard military craft.

So far as naval aviation was concerned, in the period 1910–14 most airplanes designed to take off and land on water were essentially land craft modified only to the extent necessary to allow fitting them with floats. One exception was the Sopwith "Bat-boat," a pusher biplane design, powered by a 90-hp. Austro-Daimler engine. It had a 21-foot-long planing hull constructed of cedar. Auxiliary wheels permitted landing on firm ground. In 1914, the Supermarine Aviation Works designed a flying boat, but their first try left much to be desired. In the flying boat field, at least, American practice as exemplified by Curtiss still led the way. One more airplane of the pre-war period requires consideration—the pioneering four-engine biplane designed and built in Russia by Igor Sikorsky. It was named officially the Russian Knight but was generally known as "the Grand." Weighing about 9,000 pounds fully loaded, it had a speed of about 60 mph. and was powered by four 100-hp. Argus water-cooled, in-line engines, mounted two on each side of the fuselage, one tractor and one pusher. The wing span was 92 feet and the fuselage length, 67 feet. The tail section had large multiple rudders, to assure continued control in the event of failure of one or more engines. The landing gear was made up of 16 wheels. The cabin, enormously large for the day, was completely enclosed. Its 10-minute flight, May 13, 1913, with a three-man crew headed by its designer and builder, made aerial history.

In June, 1913, the two rear engines were mounted outboard as tractors atop the leading edge of the lower wing, with improvement in both take-off and climb. In all, the Grand made 53 flights. As many as eight persons were carried on such flights, some of them two hours in length.

Early in 1914, the second of Sikorsky's four-engine biplanes was flown. Named the Ilia Mourometz, it had a span of 102 feet, and a gross weight of more than 10,000 pounds. A sister ship, built in April, was also powered by Argus engines, two rated at 140 hp. and two at 125 hp., a total of 540 hp.! With this latter airplane, Sikorsky climbed to 6,900 feet altitude, with 12 persons aboard. During the war years, about 75 of the four-engine Sikorsky biplanes were built.

On August 1, 1914, the Imperial Government of Germany declared war upon Russia and the first of the world wars was begun. Ready to play their part were perhaps 1,200 airplanes, divided about equally between the British, French and Belgian forces on the one side, and the Germans and Austrians on the other. Precisely to what uses the airplane would be put in the conflict was uncertain, even in the minds of the fiercest of the early air-power advocates.

The awful four years ahead would tell the story in painful detail. What would unfold by way of combat in the skies would underline with terrible clarity the prediction made in 1911 by one of the most capable of the early students of military aviation, Maj. Herbert Musgrove of the Royal Flying Corps: "When it comes, be assured it will come suddenly. We shall wake up one night, and find ourselves at war. . . . Another thing is certain. This war will be no walk-over. . . . In the military sphere it will be the hardest, fiercest, and bloodiest struggle we have ever had to face; let us fully make up our minds to that, and probably every one of us here tonight will take part in it. We need not be afraid of overdoing our preparations."

Less than eleven years after Wilbur and Orville Wright made history at Kitty Hawk, the airplane was flying as to war.

# 16/ THE MILITARY AIRPLANE IN 1914

*The task that we are asking from our aviators is one of the most dazzling and terrible that men have ever faced. The single combats that distinguished the age of chivalry, when champion rode against champion in front of the closing hosts, were but tame exhibitions before the starry deeds these men will have to do.*

H. G. Wells

All through the evening of Tuesday, August 4, 1914, a great, silent crowd stood facing Buckingham Palace. Minutes after the measured tones of Big Ben striking the eleventh hour had come faintly across St. James' Park, they heard the solemn announcement they had expected. Great Britain, acting as a guarantor of Belgium's integrity, had declared war on Germany.

Long since it had become tragically plain that all hope was lost to avert a great war. For years the great powers of Europe, led by Germany, had been forging giant war machines. The assassination on June 28 of the Archduke Francis Ferdinand, heir apparent to the Austrian Throne, was only the sparking of a powder keg that inevitably was destined to explode.

By August 4, the armies had been mobilized. On August 1, Germany had declared war on Russia, and on the 3d, on France. Now, the armies were marching.

That airplanes would be employed in this conflict, the first of the world wars, was obvious. Military professionals, as well as the enthusiasts, for years had discussed the proper role of aircraft in a war between the great powers of Europe. Among possible missions they had suggested were liaison, bombing, combat and reconnaissance. Of these, the last, the job of scouting enemy movements, had been given most serious consideration by the pre-war military planners.

There had been, of course, experimentation and innovation. There had been peacetime maneuvers. The airplane had been sent into a tentative sort of active service in the brush-fire wars in Tripoli and in the Balkans, but never under conditions that afforded much information of value concerning its wartime possibilities.

Now was the time to fit the new weapon into the prevailing, deep-rooted doctrines of warfare . . . to create the reality that comes in battle. As a matter af fact, there was a great deal of "fitting" to be done. What follows are jottings about the first flutterings of the airplane in World War I. While no attempt is made to provide a comprehensive account of these early successes and failures, it is to be hoped sufficient is set forth to show the kind of missions attempted by pilots flying the airplanes available for military service in the summer of 1914 (*see Chapter* XV).

On the evening of August 3—the day before England declared war—the German ambassador in Paris presented a communication to the French prime minister. It stated in part:

"The German administrative and military authorities have established a certain number of flagrantly hostile acts committed on German territory by French military aviators . . . One has attempted to destroy buildings near Wesel; others have been seen in the district of the Eifel; one has thrown bombs on the railway near Karlsruhe and Nüremberg. I am instructed and I have the honor to inform your Excellency that in the presence of these acts of aggression the German Empire considers itself in a state of war with France in consequence of the acts of the latter power."

This first significant aerial accomplishment of the war was no accomplishment at all. Wesel and Karlsruhe, and the district of the Eifel, all were so situated with respect to the frontier that French airplanes *could* have been flown as alleged. But Nüremberg! Nüremberg was nearly 250 miles from the border.

Years later in his memoirs, the German ambassador conceded the charges given as the reason for the declaration of war had been "based on disastrous mistakes." These "seem to have been merely the product of highly overwrought imagination," he wrote. His comment was, to say the least, a most charitable if unconvincing explanation. Another report of early aerial application, this one assuredly the product of "highly overwrought imagination," was a widely published story of extreme bravery. On the second day of open hostilities, so it was reported, the French pilot Roland Garros (noted for his flying exploits before and during the war) had destroyed a German Zeppelin by ramming it in flight with his monoplane at the sacrifice of his own life.

The wildest rumors were circulated, and because almost everyone was confident of military aviation's ability to perform the wondrous exploits that had been predicted, such stories were accepted without question. As time passed, however, it became obvious that most of the early reports of aerial activity had been either inaccurate or completely false.

As the British magazine *Flight* commented, "It is practically impossible to get any reliable details as to the part which is being played by aircraft in the present war, as so many of the reports received are altogether untrustworthy . . . Almost every form of aerial attack has been reported as having actually taken place—bomb dropping from airships and airplanes, and ramming of airships and airplanes by airplanes, rifle and pistol fire between airplanes, gun fire and rifle fire from the ground, etc.—and in the majority of cases it is claimed the attacks proved successful."

The plain truth is that in the opening days and weeks of the war, on both sides there was but little aerial activity, and most of this was reconnaissance.

As of the declaration of war, it is to be doubted whether the high command of either the German or the French forces felt much need for aerial reconnaissance. The grand strategy of the German Supreme Command called for a wheeling march through Belgium and Luxemburg into northern France, with the pivot the heavily fortified area around Metz. A French offensive was to be expected either to the north in southern Belgium or—and more probable—to the southeast in Lorraine. Destruction of the enemy was to be accomplished in the field wherever the issue might be joined.

The German plans especially were based on the doctrine of the *offensive à outrance*—the headlong offensive. The advance would be so bold, so determined, so rapid that strict adherence to the established attack plans was to be preferred to extemporaneous revisions in the field based upon reports likely to be tardy, incomplete, contradictory and inaccurate.

For their part, history shows the French commanders believed the rugged Meuse valley, running southeast from the Belgian border, would limit the extent of any German wheel action and that the principal enemy attack would be against the fortified area around Metz. The French generals were so sure of their hypothesis that they concentrated their troops to resist such a German advance and launched their own first offensive as if what they had thought would happen was actually taking place.

What has been written immediately above is not to say that neither side was attempting aerial reconnaissance. The fact, of course, is that the Germans and the French assigned both airplanes and dirigibles to scouting duty, as will be outlined. Rather, the purpose is to emphasize how little chance that information developed by such scouting efforts had of being seriously considered in the first days of the war.

This situation, this feeling of invincibility that made unnecessary reliance upon accurate, up-to-date information developed by reconnaissance, changed. Very quickly, it became apparent that the course of the war on the Western Front was not progressing according to the timetables of the master strategists. Once the supreme commanders realized that the successes so confidently expected were not being won, they demanded vigorous reconnaissance action—in the air—to provide them with information concerning the whereabouts and strength of the enemy. If the techniques and tools of aerial scouting needed great improvement, well, on with the job!

Before considering the use of airplanes for scouting it may be well to mention the abortive attempts by both sides to employ dirigibles on reconnaissance missions over the Western Front. The French had several airships available for duty, including two stationed at Maubeuge on the Belgian frontier. Of these, only one attempted a scouting mission. On August 21 it sallied forth only to be shot down by *French* troops who thought their enthusiastic gun fire had been directed at an enemy target.

That same day, the Germans dispatched two Zeppelins over

the Lorraine sector in an effort to obtain information that might be helpful in clearing away the massive confusion at Headquarters concerning French troop dispositions and movements in that area. The Z VII flew over a French encampment at an altitude of about 2,500 feet; fire from enemy guns did sufficient damage to cause it to crash, although the crew escaped without injury. Once airborne, the second Zeppelin, the Z VIII, was promptly fired upon by *German* troops despite earlier announcement that the flight was being scheduled. Despite some damage, the Z VIII continued on its journey into French territory. Soon it suffered from more ground fire, this time from enemy guns. This second attack resulted in mortal damage and the Zeppelin came lurching down inside the French lines. Its crew members managed to find their way on foot back to their German base.

So far as the Western Front was concerned, the dirigible was quickly proved altogether vulnerable to ground fire when sent on flights at the low altitudes considered mandatory in the war's early days for accomplishment of useful reconnaissance. On the Eastern Front, the Germans employed airships on scouting missions over Russian territory into the fall of 1914, and with rather better results.

The aerial fleets of the warring nations in the summer of 1914 had one quality in common—they were far better suited to the orderly routines of the training field than to the stepped up tempo and the unexpected emergencies that developed as soon as airplanes were flown to their wartime bases. Almost without exception, the airplanes pressed into service did well if they could cruise at 60 mph and stay in the air as long as five hours.

As the Germans advanced and as the Allies retreated, the limited capabilities of the airplanes meant hurried and repeated establishment of new bases, most of them dismal counterfeits of the well-turfed and drained fields to which the pilots were accustomed. The immediate consequence was, of course, a sharp rise in the accident rate on landing and takeoff.

Although in the beginning aerial combat—between one plane and another—was extremely rare, the early mortality rate from ground fire was alarmingly high. Partly, this was because, as wartime experience soon taught pilots, it was necessary to fly considerably higher to stay above the range of ground fire than previously had been thought necessary. Partly, it was due to the difficulty of ground forces to distinguish between aerial friend and foe. When in doubt, the soldiers blasted away.

The weather—lowering clouds, late summer thunderstorms, persistent fogs and mists—soon proved itself a grim, casualty-producing enemy to pilots of both sides. As the demand for aerial reconnaissance quickly increased, flying became a necessity in all kinds of weather that would have kept the hangar doors shut tight in the peacetime days "back home." The fact that most pilots had had little real experience in cross-country navigation and usually lacked adequate maps of the areas over which they flew, didn't help. Repeatedly, pilots lost their way and when their fuel was exhausted, were forced to come crashing down, sometimes behind the enemy lines.

The rates of attrition of personnel and equipment in the first weeks and months—due largely to the reasons cited above—were shockingly high. Actual loss of German airplanes in August 1914, alone, has been estimated officially at almost 40 per cent. Losses of Allied airplanes were similarly large.

Engine and accessory troubles, a bother that had been vexing enough at the peacetime bases, at once became a critical problem in the field. Maintenance crews weren't sufficiently trained. There weren't enough of them. It isn't known whether "spares" was a word used in 1914, but certainly there weren't enough, not by half—and those usually the wrong kind!

Maintenance problems were compounded by the large assortment of airplanes and engines in military use. In 1914, for example, the French were flying Nieuports, Deperdussins, Maurice Farmans, Voisins, Bleriots, R.E.P.'s, Caudrons, and Moranes—among others—powered by at least a half dozen different engines. The Germans were in much the same situation. Their monoplanes were products of the Rumpler, Etrich, Gotha, German Bristol, and Fokker factories. Their biplanes were the Albatros, L.V.G., Aviatik, and Otto (*see Chapter* XV).

Replacement airplanes, the ones the manufacturers (caught unprepared by the floods of new war orders) were struggling to produce in answer to urgent demands for immediate delivery, often were turned over to the military when they were still infested with the "crabs" that could have been eliminated by adequate pre-delivery flight test. The best way to describe the French and German systems designed to provide the air units in action with new airplanes and spare parts may be to say only that they were unworkable. It was months before the French first and the Germans later accomplished the necessary organization and reorganization that resulted in adequate ground services and supply for their respective air units. So far, discussion has been concerned with French and German aviation. At the beginning of the war, the Belgian air organization was small with hardly two dozen airplanes of French manufacture ready for military use. As the Germans moved across Belgium, that country's air organization became dependent upon France for equipment, and it was tied closely to the French air operation.

Except for the multi-engine Sikorsky, Russia had few if any airplanes of its own manufacture that could be assigned to military duty. Quantities of French-built airplanes had been bought and an elaborate pilot-training program had been inaugurated. Before the outbreak of fighting, the German General Staff was much impressed by Russia's "high number of well-trained airplane pilots," and expected vigorous reconnaissance and bombing action from them. Actually, the organization of Russian military aviation was so imperfect and the Russian generals were so reluctant to attempt use of anything new that little of importance was contributed in the early days by Russian airmen to the course of the war on the Eastern Front. (The Germans, incidentally, made more effective use of the airplanes for reconnaissance earlier on the Eastern Front than on the Western Front. Von Hindenburg is quoted as having said, "Without airmen, no Tannenberg.")

Within two weeks of war's outbreak, Great Britain sent 64 airplanes to France. They were B.E.-2's and -8's, Avros, Sopwith Tabloids, Henri Farmans and Bleriots (*see Chapter* XV). Casualties were suffered in the movement of air across the Channel and on to bases close to the fighting. At least five pilots and other personnel were killed and twice that number of airplanes were smashed in the operation. There were other difficulties—one pilot made a forced landing near Boulogne and was imprisoned by the French for nearly a week before he was freed.

By August 16, the Royal Flying Corps had moved to Maubeuge and on the 19th, two planes were sent on the first British reconnaissance mission of the war. The pilots, flying without observers, were ordered to perform the first segment of the mission together "so that if one was obliged to descend the other could report its whereabouts." On this leg, the planes lost their way and in the process became separated. One pilot flew over Brussels, with a population of more than 500,000, but failed to recognize it. Later he managed to locate his position correctly only to become lost again when he flew through clouds. After landing to get necessary orientation, he returned to his base 2½ hours after takeoff without having acquired information of value. The second pilot's adventure lasted eight hours during which he lost himself three times and twice landed to seek directions. He, also, was so occupied by the business of flight and navigation that he obtained little reconnaissance information. Flights of this kind seemed almost to be a rule rather than the exception.

Between August 16 and September 4, the grinding advance of the Germans forced the RFC repeatedly to select a new base. Maubeuge, Le Cateau, La Fère, Compiègne, Senlis, Juilly, Touquin, Melun . . . 10 fields in three weeks. Despite the awesome difficulties under which the RFC operated, it improved with great speed its ability to provide information about the enemy advance. This improvement in aerial reconnaissance capability was, perhaps, not greatly different from that being accomplished by French and German pilots in the same period. It was, however, first recognized and exploited on the Western Front to a significant extent by the British generals.

In his first dispatch of the war, issued September 7, the commander of the British Expeditionary Forces in Europe, Field Marshall Sir John French wrote, "I wish particularly to bring to your Lordships' notice the admirable work done by the Royal Flying Corps . . . Their skill, energy, and perseverance have been of incalculable value in the conduct of operations. Fired at constantly by both friend and foe, and not hesitating to fly in every kind of weather, they have remained undaunted throughout . . ."

The war correspondent of the *London Morning Post*, just before the war, observed that "The airplane is a wonderful instrument for reconnaissance," but doubted whether scouting activity could long be undertaken without vigorous enemy opposition appearing. "Most certainly," he wrote of the airplane, "it will, just as surely as the horseman, be challenged to fight for its information, and must be armed and equipped to accept the challenge. And where will such arming, once begun, be likely to lead us? Surely to the provision of a fleet whose primary objective must be the discovery and destruction of the enemy's aircraft. Just as the cavalry fight must often precede the search for information, and the possession of it rest with the victors, so the first effort of the Flying Corps commander will be to beat his opponent to the ground and keep the air clear for his own reconnaissance."

Predictions of this sort may well have reflected the beliefs and hopes of the military men, but such were easier said than done. For example: A German Albatros flew over Maubeuge on August 22. The RFC sent two B.E.-2's, one of them mounting a machine gun, in chase. "The machine had gotten far too long a start, and got into a rain cloud," was the laconic report. Or the case, the same day, where the RFC pilot chased another Albatros for 45 minutes in his plane equipped with a rapid-firing gun: "Was unable to get higher than 3,500 feet, while the Albatros was at about 5,000 feet. Observed no effect from the fire. As a result of this received orders to discard Lewis gun and mounting, and transfer the controls from rear seat to the front seat, the passenger to carry rifle in the back seat." Still another chase on the 22d was described: "We all turned out armed with rifles, and about six machines got ready to go up in pursuit . . . All the machines which went up were loaded with hand grenades, as the intention was to bring a hostile airplane down by dropping bombs on it. The German easily got away . . . About half an hour after the German had departed a Henri Farman of #5 Squadron, fitted with a machine gun, was still climbing steadily over the aerodrome at about 1,000 feet in a strenuous effort to catch the Boche."

Airplanes that could fly no faster or higher than their lumbering adversaries were not the answer. Nor were pistols or rifles or hand grenades the right kinds of armament to employ in aerial combat. What were needed were single-seaters, fitted with bigger engines and mounting forward-firing machine-guns. Fighter airplanes like that could and would be built.

At the outbreak of the war the heaviest load of bombs an airplane could carry was pitifully small. The bombs themselves were grenades and small artillery shells but little modified for the new use to which they were put. Bomb dropping was just that without benefit of bomb sights and, at first, without definite targets.

August 29, a German scout flew over the RFC base at Compiègne and dropped three bombs without effect. September 1, a British pilot on reconnaissance tossed two bombs at enemy cavalry gathering at a crossroads; his account cited "confusion and a stampede." September 2, two artillery shells were released from a French airplane in an effort to hit German troops in the field.

Even at this early date, efforts were being made to accomplish more with aerial bombing. Between August 30 and mid-October, German airplanes repeatedly flew over Paris, dropping small numbers of incendiaries and explosives. At the same time, other pilots dropped weighted messages, one of which read, "The German army is at the gates of Paris. There is nothing for you to do but surrender." The bombs did little harm and the messages served only to arouse indignation, but the threat of bigger bombs to come was plain.

The war's first really successful bombing raid came on October 8 when the British Naval Air Service sent two Sopwith Tabloids up from Antwerp, each armed with four 20-pound bombs. The order was to attack the dirigible sheds at Cologne and Dusseldorf. Heavy mist hid the Cologne airship base, and so the pilot dropped his bombs on the city's main railroad station without doing much damage. The second pilot found the Dusseldorf target to be in the clear, and released his bombs at 600 feet, scoring direct hits on the shed. In the ensuing fire, a new Zeppelin was destroyed. Before the end of 1914, the Germans, too, had dropped small bombs from airplanes that managed to reach the British Coast. (It was early in 1915 before the Germans sent Zeppelins on raids against Great Britain.) Similarly, the French began small air forays against cities behind the German lines. Obviously, these first attacks could affect little except morale. But plans were made for the future, and the airplanes to carry them out were laid down on the drawing boards.

Late in 1914 the forces battling on the Western Front were nearly exhausted. The grandiose plans based upon the doctrine of the *offensive à outrance* had been demolished as the armies bogged down and resorted to trench warfare.

Now it became necessary to use airplanes in scouting for information about minor military units as well as to determine the disposition of army corps and commands. At the same time, the airplane was being used to direct gunfire and to locate enemy artillery emplacements. The demands of war brought about rapid development of greatly improved photographic equipment and more reliable, lightweight radio.

The necessity to use airplanes in scouting (cavalry units were entirely unsuited for reconnaissance in a trench warfare situation) made it equally important, insofar as possible, to deny to the enemy the opportunity for aerial observation over the lines. Now, the growth of fighter types and tactics was greatly accelerated. As the opposing armies dug deeper into the chilling mud of the Western Front, their airplanes flew higher and farther. There was new purpose, new urgency, in their ranging.

With the coming of war the airplane, still a relatively frail machine, had become a matter of national importance to many nations. It was the beginning of an era of accelerated aeronautical development. The pioneer, the individual inventor-aviator began to disappear into the maw of the large manufacturer. By then, man had conquered at least the lower levels of the sea of air around him. The heritage of Kitty Hawk was established.

# POSTSCRIPT

This has been a story of the early development of the airplane. Its telling has been limited to the times of conception, birth and early growth. It reaches into the mists of antiquity, but has been concerned mostly with the pioneers who worked during the first 15 years of the Twentieth Century. It closes as the airplane was beginning to demonstrate its military potential. It has been a story of accomplishment that outstripped expectations of all but the most visionary . . . a story of beginnings that have changed the ways of the world.

# INDEX